weightwatchers 360°

Family style

180 classic, scrumptious dishes everyone will love

CHIMICHURRI-STYLE STEAK SANDWICHES p 31

about weight watchers

Weight Watchers International, Inc. is the world's leading provider of weight-management services, operating globally through a network of company-owned and franchise operations. Weight Watchers holds nearly 45,000 meetings each week worldwide, at which members receive group support and education about healthful eating patterns, behavior modification, and physical activity. Weight-loss and weight-management results vary by individual. We recommend that you attend Weight Watchers meetings to benefit from the supportive environment and follow the comprehensive Weight Watchers program, which includes a food plan, an activity plan, and a behavioral component.

WeightWatchers.com provides subscription weight-management products, such as eTools and **Weight Watchers Mobile**, and is the leading internet-based weight-management provider in the world. In addition, Weight Watchers offers a wide range of products, publications (including *Weight Watchers Magazine*, which is available on newsstands and in Weight Watchers meeting rooms), and programs for people interested in weight loss and control. For the Weight Watchers meeting nearest you, call **1-800-651-6000**. For information about bringing Weight Watchers to your workplace, call **1-800-8AT-WORK**.

Weight Watchers Publishing Group

VP, Editorial Director **Nancy Gagliardi**

Creative Director **Ed Melnitsky**

Photo Director **Deborah Hardt**

Managing Editor **Diane Pavia**

Assistant Editor **Katerina Gkionis**

Food Editor **Eileen Runyan**

Editor **Alice K. Thompson**

Recipe Developers **Patrick Decker, Lori Longbotham,
Maureen Luchejko, Jackie Plant, Carol Prager,
Alice K. Thompson**

Production Manager **Alan Biederman**

Photographer **Antonis Achilleos**

Food Stylist **Carrie Purcell**

Prop Stylist **Marina Malchin**

Art Director **Heidi North**

Designer **Laura Baer**

Art Production **Liz Trovato**

SKU #11988

Printed in the USA

Front cover: Spaghetti Squash with Garden Meatballs, page 66

Back cover: Mexicali Omelette for Two, page 4; Throw-it-in-the-Pot
Lamb Stew, page 79; Pecan Praline Cheesecake, page 212

contents

**RED, WHITE, AND GREEN
MINESTRONE** p 47

about our recipes

While losing weight isn't only about what you eat, Weight Watchers realizes the critical role it plays in your success and overall good health. That's why our philosophy is to offer great-tasting, easy recipes that are nutritious as well as delicious. We make every attempt to use wholesome ingredients and to ensure that our recipes fall within the recommendations of the U.S. Dietary Guidelines for Americans for a diet that promotes health and reduces the risk for disease. If you have special dietary needs, consult with your health-care professional for advice on a diet that is best for you, then adapt these recipes to meet your specific nutritional needs.

To achieve these good-health goals and get the maximum satisfaction from the foods you eat, we suggest you keep the following information in mind while preparing our recipes:

WEIGHT WATCHERS 360° AND GOOD NUTRITION

▶ Recipes in this book have been developed for Weight Watchers members who are following Weight Watchers 360°. **PointsPlus**® values are given for each recipe. They're assigned based on the amount of protein, carbohydrates, fat, and fiber contained in a single serving of a recipe.

▶ Recipes include approximate nutritional information: they are analyzed for Calories (Cal), Total Fat, Saturated Fat (Sat Fat), Trans Fat, Cholesterol (Chol), Sodium (Sod), Carbohydrates (Carb), Sugar, Dietary Fiber (Fib), Protein (Prot), and Calcium (Calc). The nutritional values are calculated by registered dietitians, using nutrition analysis software.

▶ Substitutions made to the ingredients will alter the per-serving nutritional information and may affect the **PointsPlus** value.

▶ Our recipes meet Weight Watchers Good Health Guidelines for eating lean proteins and fiber-rich whole grains and for having at least five servings of vegetables and fruits and two servings of low-fat or fat-free dairy products a day, while limiting your intake of saturated fat, sugar, and sodium.

▶ Health agencies recommend limiting sodium intake. To stay in line with this recommendation, we keep sodium levels in our recipes reasonably low; to boost flavor, we often include fresh herbs or a squeeze of citrus instead of salt. If you don't have to restrict your sodium, feel free to add a touch more salt as desired.

▶ In the recipes, a green triangle (▲) indicates Weight Watchers® Power Foods.

▶ Stay On Track suggestions have a **PointsPlus** value of **0** unless otherwise stated.

▶ Recipes that can be prepared in 20 minutes or less are indicated by an ⊙ icon.

▶ Recipes that are prepared in a slow cooker are indicated by an ⬚ icon.

▶ Recipes that work with the Simply Filling technique are listed on page 271. Find more details about this technique at your meeting.

▶ For information about the science behind lasting weight loss and more, please visit WeightWatchers.com/science.

CALCULATIONS NOT WHAT YOU EXPECTED?

▶ You might expect some of the *PointsPlus* values in this book to be lower when some of the foods they're made from, such as fruits and vegetables, have no *PointsPlus* values. Most fruits and veggies have no *PointsPlus* values when served as a snack or part of a meal, like a cup of berries with a sandwich. But if these foods are part of a recipe, their fiber and nutrient content are incorporated into the recipe calculations. These nutrients can affect the *PointsPlus* value.

▶ Alcohol is included in our *PointsPlus* calculations. Because alcohol information is generally not included on nutrition labels, it's not an option to include when using the hand calculator or the online calculator. But since we include alcohol information that we get from our nutritionists, you might notice discrepancies between the *PointsPlus* values you see in our recipes, and the values you get using the calculator. The *PointsPlus* values listed for our recipes are the most accurate values.

SHOPPING FOR INGREDIENTS

As you learn to eat healthier and add more Weight Watchers Power Foods to your meals, remember these tips for choosing foods wisely:

Lean Meats and Poultry Purchase lean meats and poultry, and trim them of all visible fat before cooking. When poultry is cooked with the skin on, we recommend removing the skin before eating. Nutritional information for recipes that include meat, poultry, and fish is based on cooked, skinless boneless portions (unless otherwise stated), with the fat trimmed.

Seafood Whenever possible, our recipes call for seafood that is sustainable and deemed the most healthful for human consumption so that your choice of seafood is not only good for the oceans but also good for you. For more information about the best seafood choices and to download a pocket guide, go to environmentaldefensefund.org or montereybayaquarium.org. For information about mercury and seafood go to weightwatchers.com.

Produce For best flavor, maximum nutrient content, and the lowest prices, buy fresh local produce, such as vegetables, leafy greens, and fruits, in season. Rinse them thoroughly before using, and keep a supply of cut-up vegetables and fruits in your refrigerator for convenient healthy snacks.

Whole Grains Explore your market for whole-grain products such as whole wheat and whole-grain breads and pastas, brown rice, bulgur, barley, cornmeal, whole wheat couscous, oats, and quinoa to enjoy with your meals.

PREPARATION AND MEASURING

Read the Recipe Take a couple of minutes to read through the ingredients and directions before you start to prepare a recipe. This will prevent you from discovering midway through that you don't have an important ingredient or that a recipe requires several hours of marinating. And it's also a good idea to assemble all ingredients and utensils within easy reach before you begin a recipe.

Weighing and Measuring The success of any recipe depends on accurate weighing and measuring. The effectiveness of the Weight Watchers Program and the accuracy of the nutritional analysis depend on correct measuring as well. Use the following techniques:

▶ Weigh foods such as meat, poultry, and fish on a food scale.

▶ To measure liquids, use a standard glass or plastic measuring cup placed on a level surface. For amounts less than ¼ cup, use standard measuring spoons.

▶ To measure dry ingredients, use metal or plastic measuring cups that come in ¼-, ⅓-, ½-, and 1-cup sizes. Fill the appropriate cup, and level it with the flat edge of a knife or spatula. For amounts less than ¼ cup, use standard measuring spoons.

Chapter 1

hearty breakfasts & brunches

hearty breakfasts & brunches

gruyère and asparagus frittata

SERVES 4

2 teaspoons olive oil

1 shallot, minced

▲ **10 asparagus spears, trimmed and cut into 1-inch pieces**

▲ **4 large eggs**

▲ **2 large egg whites**

1 tablespoon water

¼ teaspoon salt

¼ cup shredded Gruyère cheese

1 Preheat broiler.

2 Heat oil in 10-inch ovenproof skillet over medium-high heat. Add shallot and asparagus, and cook, stirring frequently, until vegetables soften, about 4 minutes.

3 Meanwhile, beat eggs, egg whites, water, salt, and pepper in medium bowl until frothy. Stir in Gruyère cheese. Pour over asparagus mixture, stirring gently to combine. Reduce heat to medium; cover and cook until eggs are set, 6–7 minutes.

4 Place skillet under broiler. Broil 5 inches from heat until top of frittata is lightly browned, about 1 minute. Let stand 2 minutes before cutting into 4 wedges.

Per serving (1 wedge): 140 Cal, 9 g Total Fat, 3 g Sat Fat, 0 g Trans Fat, 222 mg Chol, 261 mg Sod, 4 g Carb, 1 g Sugar, 1 g Fib, 11 g Prot, 102 mg Calc.

Stay On Track
Slice ripe tomatoes, then sprinkle them with balsamic vinegar and a pinch of salt and pepper for a tasty and colorful accompaniment to this delicious egg dish.

mexicali omelette for two

SERVES 2

Ingredients

- 1 cup fat-free egg substitute
- 1 tablespoon water
- ⅛ teaspoon salt
- ⅛ teaspoon black pepper
- 1 teaspoon canola oil
- ¼ cup fat-free salsa verde
- ¼ small avocado, pitted, peeled, and thinly sliced
- 3 tablespoons shredded fat-free Monterey Jack cheese
- ½ small plum tomato, diced
- Fresh cilantro for garnish

1 Beat egg substitute, water, salt, and pepper in medium bowl until frothy.

2 Heat oil in medium nonstick skillet over medium heat. Pour in egg mixture and cook, stirring gently, until underside is set, about 2 minutes. Spread salsa evenly over half of omelette. Top with avocado, Monterey Jack cheese, and tomato. With spatula, fold other half over filling. Continue to cook until filling is heated through and eggs are set, 2–3 minutes.

3 Slide omelette onto plate and cut in half. Sprinkle with cilantro.

Per serving (½ omelette): 143 Cal, 6 g Total Fat, 1 g Sat Fat, 0 g Trans Fat, 2 mg Chol, 608 mg Sod, 6 g Carb, 2 g Sugar, 2 g Fib, 17 g Prot, 345 mg Calc.

**MEXICALI OMELETTE
FOR TWO**

open-face egg-and-ricotta english muffins

SERVES 4

- ▲ **4 large eggs**
- ▲ **4 large egg whites**
- **1 tablespoon chopped fresh chives**
- **1 teaspoon chopped fresh thyme**
- **⅛ teaspoon salt**
- **⅛ teaspoon black pepper**
- **1 teaspoon olive oil**
- **½ cup part-skim ricotta cheese**
- **2 whole wheat English muffins, split and toasted**

1 Beat eggs, egg whites, chives, thyme, salt, and pepper in medium bowl until frothy.

2 Heat oil in large nonstick skillet over medium heat. Add egg mixture and cook, stirring, until eggs start to set, about 1 minute. Add ricotta and cook, stirring, until eggs are cooked through, about 2 minutes. Divide egg mixture evenly among muffin halves and serve.

Per serving (½ cup egg mixture and 1 muffin half):
207 Cal, 9 g Total Fat, 3 g Sat Fat, 0 g Trans Fat, 225 mg Chol, 442 mg Sod, 16 g Carb, 3 g Sugar, 2 g Fib, 16 g Prot, 196 mg Calc.

For Your Information
Instead of separating eggs for recipes, save time by purchasing a carton of egg whites from the dairy section of your supermarket. Two tablespoons are equal to about one large egg white.

bacon-and-swiss coddled eggs

SERVES 4

- ▲ **½ cup thawed frozen spinach, squeezed dry**
- ▲ **4 large eggs**
- **¼ teaspoon black pepper**
- **⅛ teaspoon salt**
- **4 slices Canadian bacon**
- ▲ **4 tablespoons shredded fat-free Swiss cheese**

1 Preheat oven to 350°F. Spray 4 (8-ounce) ramekins or custard cups with nonstick spray; place on small rimmed baking sheet.

2 Place one-fourth of spinach in bottom of each ramekin. Beat eggs with pepper and salt in medium bowl until frothy; pour evenly into ramekins. Top each cup with a slice of bacon and 1 tablespoon Swiss cheese. Bake until eggs are just set, about 20 minutes.

Per serving (1 ramekin): 139 Cal, 7 g Total Fat, 2 g Sat Fat, 0 g Trans Fat, 230 mg Chol, 625 mg Sod, 3 g Carb, 1 g Sugar, 1 g Fib, 16 g Prot, 248 mg Calc.

Make Ahead

Assemble the egg ramekins; cover and refrigerate up to 2 days ahead. Uncover and let stand at room temperature 10 minutes before baking.

poached eggs in portobello cups
SERVES 4

- ▲ **4 medium Portobello mushroom caps**
- ▲ **2 leeks, cleaned and thinly sliced, white parts only**
- **2 teaspoons olive oil**
- **1 tablespoon sherry vinegar or balsamic vinegar**
- **¼ teaspoon salt**
- **¼ teaspoon black pepper**
- ▲ **1 cup lightly packed baby arugula**
- **¼ cup goat cheese, crumbled**
- ▲ **4 large eggs**

1 Preheat oven to 450°F. Spray mushroom caps on both sides with nonstick spray, and place, gill sides up, on baking sheet. Toss leeks with oil, vinegar, salt, and pepper in small bowl. Divide leeks evenly among mushroom caps. Bake until mushrooms are just tender, about 12 minutes.

2 Divide arugula among mushroom caps; top each with 1 tablespoon goat cheese. Return mushrooms to oven and bake until arugula has wilted and cheese is soft, about 3 minutes.

3 Meanwhile, bring 2 inches of water to boil in deep skillet. Place 4 small cups on work surface. Crack 1 egg into each cup. Holding one cup close to surface of simmering water, slip egg into water. Repeat with remaining eggs. Simmer until egg whites are set and yolks begin to thicken but are not hard, 3–4 minutes. Remove eggs from water with slotted spoon and place 1 egg on top of each mushroom cap.

Per serving (1 filled mushroom cap and 1 poached egg): 163 Cal, 9 g Total Fat, 3 g Sat Fat, 0 g Trans Fat, 218 mg Chol, 253 mg Sod, 13 g Carb, 4 g Sugar, 2 g Fib, 10 g Prot, 73 mg Calc.

For Your Information
Leeks can be gritty, so be sure to rinse them after slicing. You can place them in a large bowl of water and swish them around, then allow any sand to settle to the bottom. Lift the leeks out with a slotted spoon and pat dry.

slow-cooker apple-and-sausage strata

SERVES 12

1 teaspoon canola oil

12 ounces frozen skinless turkey breakfast sausages, chopped

▲ 2 medium Vidalia or other sweet onions, chopped

▲ 2 Fuji apples, cored and grated

▲ 8 large eggs

▲ 4 egg whites

▲ 3 cups fat-free milk

▲ 1 cup fat-free half-and-half

¼ teaspoon salt

¼ teaspoon black pepper

12 slices stone-ground 100% whole wheat bread, diced (about 6 cups)

1 cup shredded reduced-fat Jarlsberg cheese

1 Spray 5- or 6-quart slow cooker with nonstick spray.

2 Heat oil in large skillet over medium-high heat. Add sausage (it does not need to be thawed) and onions. Cook, stirring frequently, until onions have softened and sausage is cooked through, 4–5 minutes. Remove from heat and stir in apples.

3 Beat eggs, egg whites, milk, half-and-half, salt, and pepper in large bowl until frothy. Spread 2 cups bread on bottom of prepared slow cooker. Top with half of sausage mixture and sprinkle with 1/3 cup Jarlsberg cheese. Repeat with 2 cups bread, remaining sausage mixture, and 1/3 cup cheese. Finish layering with remaining bread and remaining 1/3 cup cheese. Pour egg mixture over layers; cover and refrigerate slow cooker crock at least 1 hour or overnight.

4 Set crock back into heating unit, and cook until eggs are completely set, 2 ½–3 hours on high.

Per serving (scant 1 cup strata): 300 Cal, 11 g Total Fat, 3 g Sat Fat, 0 g Trans Fat, 194 mg Chol, 504 mg Sod, 31 g Carb, 12 g Sugar, 3 g Fib, 20 g Prot, 268 mg Calc.

Make Ahead

This classic egg casserole is loaded with sausage, cheese, and a sweet hint of apple, all baked with whole wheat bread in a rich egg custard. It's a perfect brunch for a crowd, and you can put it together through step 3 up to 1 day ahead.

**CREAMY SLOW-COOKER GRITS
WITH EGGS AND COLLARDS**

creamy slow-cooker grits with eggs and collards

SERVES 6

GRITS

- 1 cup stone-ground grits (not quick cooking)
- 2 cups water
- 2 cups fat-free milk
- ¼ teaspoon salt
- ½ cup fat-free half-and-half

EGGS AND COLLARDS

- 2 teaspoons olive oil
- 1 onion, diced
- 1 large red bell pepper, diced
- 1 (16-ounce) bag frozen chopped collard greens, thawed and squeezed dry
- ¼ teaspoon salt
- ¼ teaspoon black pepper
- 6 large eggs

1 To make grits, combine grits, water, milk, and salt in 5- or 6-quart slow cooker. Cover and cook on low 8 hours. Remove lid and stir in half-and-half, stirring until smooth.

2 To make eggs and collards, heat oil in large skillet over medium-high heat. Add onion and bell pepper, and cook, stirring frequently, until vegetables soften, about 5 minutes. Add collard greens, salt, and black pepper; cook, stirring frequently, until greens are tender, about 7 minutes. Transfer vegetable mixture to medium bowl and keep warm.

3 Wipe skillet out with paper towel. Spray with nonstick spray and set over medium heat. Add 3 eggs to skillet; cover and cook until yolks are slightly set and whites are completely cooked through, about 3 minutes. Repeat with remaining 3 eggs, spraying pan with more nonstick spray if necessary.

4 Meanwhile, divide grits and vegetable mixture among serving bowls. Top each bowl with an egg.

Per serving (⅔ cup grits, ½ cup collard greens, and **1 egg):** 252 Cal, 6 g Total Fat, 2 g Sat Fat, 0 g Trans Fat, 216 mg Chol, 450 mg Sod, 36 g Carb, 8 g Sugar, 4 g Fib, 14 g Prot, 312 mg Calc.

hearty buttermilk flapjacks with peaches
SERVES 4

½ cup whole wheat flour

⅓ cup all-purpose flour

¼ cup quick-cooking oats

2 tablespoons wheat germ

2 teaspoons sugar

1 teaspoon baking powder

¼ teaspoon baking soda

¼ teaspoon salt

1 ½ cups low-fat buttermilk

▲ 1 large egg

1 teaspoon vanilla extract

▲ 2 ripe medium peaches, peeled, pitted, and sliced

1 teaspoon honey

1 teaspoon lemon juice

1 teaspoon canola oil

1 Combine whole wheat flour, all-purpose flour, oats, wheat germ, sugar, baking powder, baking soda, and salt in medium bowl. Whisk together buttermilk, egg, and vanilla in another bowl. Add buttermilk mixture to flour mixture, stirring just until blended. Set aside 5 minutes.

2 Meanwhile, combine peaches, honey, and lemon juice in medium bowl and toss.

3 Heat ½ teaspoon oil in large nonstick skillet over medium heat. Stir batter; pour by ¼ cupfuls into pan, making 4 pancakes. Cook until bubbles appear at edges of pancakes and undersides are golden, 2–3 minutes. Flip and cook 2 minutes longer. Repeat with remaining batter, making total of 12 pancakes and adding an additional ¼ teaspoon oil to the pan between each batch. Serve with peaches.

Per serving (3 pancakes and ⅓ cup peaches): 242 Cal, 4 g Total Fat, 1 g Sat Fat, 0 g Trans Fat, 57 mg Chol, 475 mg Sod, 41 g Carb, 14 g Sugar, 5 g Fib, 10 g Prot, 143 mg Calc.

For Your Information
These tender, flavorful pancakes cook up very thick. If you like thinner pancakes, stir 2 tablespoons of water into the batter. If fresh peaches aren't in season, use 1 ⅓ cups thawed frozen unsweetened peach slices.

buckwheat crêpes with mushrooms and goat cheese

SERVES 4

- ¾ cup fat-free milk
- ½ cup water
- ½ cup buckwheat flour
- ¼ cup all-purpose flour
- 1 large egg
- ¼ teaspoon salt
- 1 teaspoon canola oil
- ¾ pound cremini mushrooms, sliced
- 3 shallots, finely chopped
- 2 cups frozen chopped spinach, thawed and squeezed dry
- ½ cup crumbled goat cheese
- ¼ teaspoon ground nutmeg
- ¼ cup low-fat sour cream
- 2 tablespoons grated Parmesan cheese

1 To make crêpes, whisk together milk, water, buckwheat flour, all-purpose flour, egg, and salt in medium bowl until smooth.

2 Spray crêpe pan or small (6- or 7-inch) skillet with nonstick spray and set over medium heat until drop of water sizzles on it. Stir batter; pour scant ¼ cup batter into center of pan, tilting pan to coat bottom with batter. Cook until top is set and underside is golden, 1–2 minutes. Flip and cook until golden brown, about 30 seconds. Slide crêpe onto wax paper. Lightly spray pan and repeat with remaining batter, making total of 8 crêpes, spraying pan each time before adding more batter.

3 Preheat oven to 375°F. Spray 7 x 11-inch baking dish with nonstick spray.

4 Heat oil in large nonstick skillet over medium heat. Add mushrooms and shallots. Cook, stirring occasionally, until mushrooms are tender, 8–10 minutes. Stir in spinach. Transfer to bowl and cool slightly. Stir in goat cheese and nutmeg.

5 Spoon about ⅓ cup mushroom mixture on each crêpe. Roll up crêpes and place, seam side down, in prepared baking dish. Spread sour cream over top and sprinkle with Parmesan. Bake until Parmesan is lightly browned and filling is heated through, 20–25 minutes. Cool 10 minutes before serving.

Per serving (2 filled crêpes): 243 Cal, 7 g Total Fat, 3 g Sat Fat, 0 g Trans Fat, 65 mg Chol, 350 mg Sod, 31 g Carb, 6 g Sugar, 5 g Fib, 15 g Prot, 263 mg Calc.

Make Ahead
If you like, prepare the crêpes up to 2 days in advance. Wrap them well, keeping layers of wax paper in between, and refrigerate.

baked french toast with strawberry sauce

SERVES 6

- 1 (12-inch) whole wheat baguette
- ▲ 3 large eggs
- ▲ 3 large egg whites
- ▲ 1 ¼ cups fat-free milk
- 1 ½ tablespoons brown sugar
- 1 teaspoon vanilla extract
- ¾ teaspoon ground cinnamon
- ¼ teaspoon salt
- ▲ 1 pound strawberries, hulled and sliced
- 1 ½ tablespoons granulated sugar
- 2 teaspoons lemon juice

1 Spray 9 x 13-inch baking dish with nonstick spray. Cut baguette into 18 (²/₃-inch-thick) slices.

2 Whisk together eggs, egg whites, milk, brown sugar, vanilla, cinnamon, and salt in large bowl. Dip bread slices in egg mixture, turning to coat evenly. Arrange slices in prepared baking dish, overlapping if necessary. Pour remaining egg mixture over bread slices. Cover and refrigerate at least 30 minutes or overnight.

3 Preheat oven to 400°F. Bake casserole until toast is cooked through and top is lightly browned, about 20 minutes.

4 Meanwhile, set 1 ¼ cups sliced strawberries aside. Combine remaining strawberries and granulated sugar in small saucepan over medium-high heat. Cook, stirring frequently, until sugar has dissolved and berries are very soft, 4–5 minutes. Transfer mixture to blender and puree. Pour into medium serving bowl; stir in lemon juice and reserved strawberries. Serve over toast.

Per serving (3 pieces toast and ¼ cup strawberry sauce): 183 Cal, 3 g Total Fat, 1 g Sat Fat, 0 g Trans Fat, 109 mg Chol, 335 mg Sod, 30 g Carb, 13 g Sugar, 3 g Fib, 10 g Prot, 93 mg Calc.

**BAKED FRENCH TOAST
WITH STRAWBERRY SAUCE**

breakfast pizza

SERVES 6

- 2 teaspoons cornmeal
- 1 (15-ounce) ball whole wheat pizza dough, thawed if frozen
- ½ cup shredded part-skim, reduced-sodium mozzarella cheese
- 4 slices turkey bacon, coarsely chopped
- ⅓ cup sun-dried tomato halves (not packed in oil), sliced
- 3 scallions, trimmed and chopped
- ¼ cup fresh parsley leaves, chopped

1 Spray large baking sheet with nonstick spray and sprinkle with cornmeal.

2 On floured surface with lightly floured rolling pin, roll dough into 11 x 13-inch rectangle. Transfer to prepared baking sheet, gently reshaping dough as necessary. Cover loosely with plastic wrap and let rise in warm place 30 minutes.

3 Position rack in bottom third of oven. Preheat oven to 450°F.

4 Bake crust 5 minutes. Remove from oven. Sprinkle mozzarella cheese evenly over crust. Top with bacon, tomatoes, and scallions. Bake until crust is browned and cooked through, 7–8 minutes. Sprinkle with parsley and cut into 6 pieces.

Per serving (1 piece pizza): 239 Cal, 6 g Total Fat, 2 g Sat Fat, 0 g Trans Fat, 14 mg Chol, 579 mg Sod, 34 g Carb, 1 g Sugar, 4 g Fib, 11 g Prot, 107 mg Calc.

whole-grain blueberry muffins with lemon crumb topping

SERVES 12

1 ½ cups + 1 tablespoon white whole wheat flour

⅓ cup + 2 tablespoons sugar

1 tablespoon cold unsalted butter, diced

Zest of 1 lemon

½ cup quick-cooking oats

¼ cup wheat germ

1 ½ teaspoons baking powder

1 teaspoon baking soda

¼ teaspoon salt

1 ¼ cups fresh or frozen unsweetened blueberries

1 cup low-fat buttermilk

1 large egg

1 tablespoon canola oil

1 teaspoon vanilla extract

1 Preheat oven to 375°F. Line 12-cup muffin pan with paper liners. Combine 1 tablespoon flour, 2 tablespoons sugar, butter, and lemon zest in small bowl. Set aside.

2 Whisk together remaining 1 ½ cups flour, remaining ⅓ cup sugar, oats, wheat germ, baking powder, baking soda, and salt in large bowl. Stir in blueberries. Whisk together buttermilk, egg, oil, and vanilla in another bowl. Add buttermilk mixture to flour mixture and stir just until blended.

3 Spoon batter evenly into prepared muffin cups. Sprinkle tops evenly with lemon crumb mixture. Bake until toothpick inserted into muffin comes out clean, 22–24 minutes. Cool in pan on rack 5 minutes; remove muffins from pan and cool completely on rack.

Per serving (1 muffin): 149 Cal, 4 g Total Fat, 1 g Sat Fat, 0 g Trans Fat, 21 mg Chol, 250 mg Sod, 25 g Carb, 9 g Sugar, 3 g Fib, 5 g Prot, 43 mg Calc.

Make Ahead

These muffins will keep in an airtight container up to 2 days, or your can freeze them in a zip-close plastic freezer bag up to 3 months. Frozen muffins can be reheated, unwrapped, in a 325°F oven until warmed through.

chewy oat and three-seed breakfast bars

SERVES 12

1 ¼ cups old-fashioned rolled oats

⅓ cup raw unsalted sunflower seeds

¼ cup raw pepitas (green pumpkin seeds)

2 tablespoons flaxseeds

2 cups whole-grain puffed wheat cereal

½ cup chopped dried apricots

⅓ cup dried blueberries

¼ cup almond butter

3 tablespoons honey

3 tablespoons brown sugar

1 teaspoon vanilla extract

¼ teaspoon salt

1 Preheat oven to 350°F. Spray 8-inch-square baking pan with nonstick spray.

2 Spread oats, sunflower seeds, pepitas, and flaxseeds on large rimmed baking sheet. Bake, shaking pan halfway through baking, until oats are lightly toasted and seeds are fragrant, about 8 minutes. Transfer mixture to large bowl. Add cereal, apricots, and blueberries; toss to combine.

3 Combine almond butter, honey, brown sugar, vanilla, and salt in small saucepan. Set over medium-low heat and cook, stirring frequently, until mixture bubbles around edges of pan, 3–4 minutes. Pour almond butter mixture over cereal mixture and stir until combined. Scrape into prepared pan. Coat hands with nonstick spray and press mixture down firmly to make an even layer. Refrigerate until firm, about 30 minutes. Cut into 12 bars.

Per serving (1 bar): 181 Cal, 8 g Total Fat, 1 g Sat Fat, 0 g Trans Fat, 1 mg Chol, 77 mg Sod, 25 g Carb, 13 g Sugar, 3 g Fib, 5 g Prot, 27 mg Calc.

Make Ahead

These bars are great to pack up with a piece of fresh fruit for breakfasts on the go. They'll keep refrigerated up to 1 week.

savory steel-cut oats with bacon and kale

SERVES 4

1 ½ teaspoons olive oil

4 scallions, sliced

1 clove garlic, finely chopped

1 cup steel-cut oats

1 cup frozen chopped kale

3 cups water

½ teaspoon salt

3 slices cooked turkey bacon, diced

1 Heat oil in medium saucepan over medium heat. Add scallions and garlic, and cook, stirring occasionally, until softened, about 3 minutes. Stir in oats, stirring until coated. Add kale, water, and salt; bring to boil. Reduce heat; cover and simmer until oats are very tender and most of liquid has been absorbed, 50-60 minutes.

2 Remove from heat and let stand, covered, 5 minutes. Serve sprinkled with bacon.

Per serving (1 cup oats and 1 tablespoon crumbled bacon): 152 Cal, 6 g Total Fat, 1 g Sat Fat, 0 g Trans Fat, 10 mg Chol, 498 mg Sod, 18 g Carb, 1 g Sugar, 4 g Fib, 7 g Prot, 96 mg Calc.

For Your Information

Here's the perfect break from sweet breakfast cereals. If you're not a bacon fan, you can omit it and instead garnish the dish with 4 tablespoons chopped almonds (1 tablespoon per serving) with no change in the **PointsPlus** value.

WHOLE-GRAIN BLUEBERRY MUFFINS WITH LEMON CRUMB TOPPING p 17

PEAR AND PECAN SCONES

CHEWY OAT AND THREE-SEED BREAKFAST BARS p 18

pear and pecan scones
SERVES 6

¾ cup + 2 tablespoons whole wheat pastry flour

¼ cup quick-cooking oats

2 tablespoons ground flaxseed

1 tablespoon + 1 teaspoon granulated sugar

1 teaspoon baking powder

¼ teaspoon baking soda

¼ teaspoon salt

1 ½ tablespoons cold light cream cheese (Neufchâtel), cut into small pieces

1 tablespoon cold unsalted butter, diced

1 pear, peeled, cored, and finely diced

3 tablespoons finely chopped pecans

⅓ cup + 1 tablespoon low-fat buttermilk

1 large egg white

1 Preheat oven to 375°F. Spray small baking sheet with nonstick spray.

2 Whisk together flour, oats, flaxseed, 1 tablespoon sugar, baking powder, baking soda, and salt in medium bowl. With pastry blender or 2 knives used scissor-fashion, cut in cream cheese and butter until mixture resembles fine crumbs. Gently stir in pear and 2 tablespoons pecans. Whisk ⅓ cup buttermilk and egg white together in small bowl. Add to flour mixture and stir just until flour mixture is moistened (dough will be soft).

3 Gather dough into ball and place on floured surface. Knead just until dough comes together, 2–3 times. Gather into a ball and place on prepared baking sheet. Pat into 7-inch round. Brush dough with remaining 1 tablespoon buttermilk; sprinkle evenly with remaining 1 teaspoon sugar and remaining 1 tablespoon pecans.

4 Spray long, thin knife with nonstick spray; cut round into 6 wedges (do not separate wedges). Bake until toothpick inserted into center comes out clean, 20–25 minutes. Let cool on baking sheet on rack 10 minutes. Separate wedges and serve warm.

Per serving (1 scone): 134 Cal, 6 g Total Fat, 2 g Sat Fat, 0 g Trans Fat, 8 mg Chol, 285 mg Sod, 18 g Carb, 6 g Sugar, 3 g Fib, 4 g Prot, 54 mg Calc.

Make Ahead
You can freeze these scones to have on hand for quick breakfasts: Cool them completely on a rack, then wrap each in plastic wrap and freeze up to 3 months. To reheat, unwrap scones and place in a 300°F oven until warmed through.

5 WAYS TO BOOST YOUR BREAKFAST

The verdict is unanimous: Start with a good breakfast, and you're much more likely to stick to a healthy eating plan throughout the day. Here are five strategies that can help you make the most of your morning meal.

Plan ahead. Spend a little time over the weekend organizing your a.m. routine. Do your mornings turn hectic, leaving you no time to sit down? If so, plan to make up some grab-and-go options like Chewy Oat and Three-Seed Breakfast Bars (page 18) and Piña Colada Breakfast Cups (page 25).

Think protein. A healthy dose of protein can keep you feeling full and satisfied throughout the morning. If your favorite breakfasts are a little light on protein, consider these easy additions, all of which clock in at *2 PointsPlus* value:

> **1 large hard-cooked egg**
> **⅔ cup plain fat-free Greek yogurt**
> **2 tablespoons sliced almonds**
> **2 ounces fat-free Cheddar cheese**
> **2 ounces lean ham**

Start or finish with fruit. Commit to including at least one serving of fruit with your breakfast. It's easy to top your cereal with berries or a sliced banana, or try a broiled half grapefruit or a single-serve container of unsweetened applesauce. Stock frozen unsweetened fruits in your freezer to make sure you always have something on hand in the morning.

Experiment with whole grains. Go beyond oats and try quick-cooking, flavorful grains like kasha, bulgur, quinoa, and millet in your breakfast bowl. They're delicious topped with milk or a nondairy beverage. Add fruit, and you may not even need a sweetener.

Reward a new habit. Commit to improving your morning meal in at least one way for a week, then schedule something to look forward to: Get yourself a snazzy new travel mug, plan a fun outing with friends or family or just by yourself, or treat yourself to coffee and the newspaper in bed for a relaxed weekend morning.

maple-brown rice breakfast pudding

SERVES 4

- ▲ **2 cups plain unsweetened soy milk**
- ▲ **¾ cup brown rice**
- **¼ cup raisins**
- **1 tablespoon maple syrup**
- **½ teaspoon vanilla extract**
- **½ teaspoon cinnamon**

1 Bring soy milk to boil in medium saucepan over medium-high heat. Stir in rice, raisins, maple syrup, and vanilla. Bring back to boil, stir again, and reduce heat to medium-low. Cover and simmer until most of liquid has evaporated, about 45 minutes.

2 Remove from heat and let stand until rice is very tender, about 10 minutes. Sprinkle with cinnamon and divide among 4 bowls.

Per serving (⅔ cup): 242 Cal, 4 g Total Fat, 1 g Sat Fat, 0 g Trans Fat, 0 mg Chol, 7 mg Sod, 42 g Carb, 11 g Sugar, 3 g Fib, 9 g Prot, 48 mg Calc.

Stay On Track

For an even more filling breakfast, top each serving with fruit: The flavors of bananas, apples, or pears will harmonize particularly well with the maple and cinnamon in this healthful breakfast.

multigrain slow-cooker porridge

6 cups plain unsweetened almond milk

2 ½ cups water

2 teaspoons vanilla extract

1 (2-inch) piece fresh ginger, quartered

¾ teaspoon salt

▲ **¾ cup pearl barley**

▲ **¾ cup steel-cut oats**

▲ **½ cup quinoa, rinsed**

▲ **2 large mangos, peeled, seeded, and diced**

1 Combine almond milk, water, vanilla, ginger, and salt in a 5- to 6-quart slow cooker. Stir in barley, oats, and quinoa. Cover and cook on low until grains are very soft, 7–8 hours.

2 Remove ginger pieces and discard. Serve porridge with mangos.

Per serving (⅔ cup porridge and 3 tablespoons diced **mango):** 134 Cal, 2 g Total Fat, 0 g Sat Fat, 0 g Trans Fat, 0 mg Chol, 240 mg Sod, 25 g Carb, 5 g Sugar, 4 g Fib, 4 g Prot, 112 mg Calc.

Make Ahead

Freeze leftovers in single-serve portions in zip-close plastic freezer bags up to 3 months. To reheat, remove porridge from bag and place in microwave-safe bowl. Microwave on Medium until hot, 2 to 3 minutes, stirring once or twice.

piña colada breakfast cups
SERVES 4

2 tablespoons unsweetened shredded coconut

2 tablespoons ground flaxseed

▲ **1 ½ cups fat-free cottage cheese**

½ cup vanilla fat-free yogurt

⅛ teaspoon ground nutmeg

▲ **1 ⅓ cups diced fresh pineapple or canned unsweetened pineapple in juice**

1 Preheat oven to 350°F. Line a baking pan with foil. Sprinkle coconut and flaxseed on foil and bake until coconut is golden, 5–6 minutes.

2 Combine cottage cheese, yogurt, and nutmeg in a medium bowl. Divide among 4 bowls; top with pineapple and sprinkle with coconut mixture.

Per serving (½ cup cottage cheese mixture, ⅓ cup pineapple, and 1 tablespoon coconut mixture): 142 Cal, 3 g Total Fat, 2 g Sat Fat, 0 g Trans Fat, 4 mg Chol, 342 mg Sod, 16 g Carb, 12 g Sugar, 2 g Fib, 12 g Prot, 96 mg Calc.

For Your Information
Contrary to popular belief, pineapples do not ripen after harvesting, so make sure the one you select is ready for eating. The skin should be bright and slightly shiny, not dull, and the leaves at the top should be crisp and green. Sniff the base; it should smell rich and sweet.

Chapter 2

satisfying sandwiches, soups & salads

satisfying sandwiches, soups & salads

open-face pear, prosciutto, and blue cheese sandwiches

SERVES 2

1 large firm-ripe pear, quartered, cored, and sliced

2 slices country wheat bread, toasted

2 thin slices prosciutto

1 ounce Gorgonzola or other blue cheese, crumbled

2 teaspoons honey

1 Spray large skillet with nonstick spray and set over medium heat. Add pear slices in single layer and cook until lightly browned, about 2 minutes per side.

2 Place pear slices evenly on bread. Top each sandwich with prosciutto, sprinkle with Gorgonzola, and drizzle with honey. Serve at once.

Per serving (1 sandwich): 288 Cal, 8 g Total Fat, 5 g Sat Fat, 0 g Trans Fat, 27 mg Chol, 791 mg Sod, 47 g Carb, 22 g Sugar, 5 g Fib, 10 g Prot, 386 mg Calc.

Stay On Track

Tender, nutrient-packed greens like watercress or pea shoots are an excellent addition to these sandwiches. You can add a handful to each sandwich just before you drizzle them with honey.

**CHIMICHURRI-STYLE
STEAK SANDWICHES**

chimichurri-style steak sandwiches
SERVES 4

- 1 (½-pound) lean flank steak, trimmed
- ¼ teaspoon kosher salt
- 1 tomato, diced
- ½ cup chopped fresh parsley
- 1 ½ teaspoons olive oil
- 1 ½ teaspoons red-wine vinegar
- 1 garlic clove, minced
- ¼ teaspoon dried oregano, crushed
- 1 small (8-ounce) multigrain baguette
- 2 tablespoons fat-free mayonnaise
- 4 red leaf lettuce leaves

1 Sprinkle steak with ⅛ teaspoon salt. Spray ridged grill pan with nonstick spray and set over medium-high heat until very hot. Place steak in pan and grill until browned and instant-read thermometer inserted into side of steak registers 145°F for medium, 4–5 minutes per side. Transfer steak to cutting board and let stand 5 minutes.

2 Meanwhile, to make chimichurri, combine tomato, parsley, oil, vinegar, garlic, oregano, and remaining ⅛ teaspoon salt in small bowl.

3 Split baguette lengthwise without cutting completely through. Remove soft center from baguette and discard (or save for bread crumbs). Spread mayonnaise on cut sides of baguette.

4 Thinly slice steak across grain. Layer lettuce and steak on bottom of bread. Spoon chimichurri evenly over steak. Cover with remaining half and cut baguette into 4 equal sandwiches.

Per serving (1 sandwich): 289 Cal, 8 g Total Fat, 2 g Sat Fat, 0 g Trans Fat, 29 mg Chol, 536 mg Sod, 32 g Carb, 4 g Sugar, 4 g Fib, 23 g Prot, 31 mg Calc.

For Your Information
Chimichurri, a classic sauce from Argentina, is used as both a condiment and marinade for grilled meats. Always prepared with parsley and vinegar, we added tomato, but you can also stir in paprika or ground cumin.

chicken wraps with tangy slaw

SERVES 4

Zest of ½ lime

1 ½ teaspoons paprika

1 teaspoon olive oil

1 garlic clove, minced

¼ teaspoon salt

Pinch cayenne

▲ ¾ pound chicken breast tenders

▲ 2 tablespoons plain fat-free yogurt

1 tablespoon low-fat mayonnaise

2 tablespoons chopped fresh cilantro

2 teaspoons lime juice

▲ 2 cups coleslaw mix

▲ 2 large radishes, shredded

4 (1 ½-ounce) lavash breads

▲ 1 ⅓ cups mixed salad greens

1 Line broiler pan with foil; preheat broiler. Combine lime zest, paprika, oil, garlic, ⅛ teaspoon salt, and cayenne in medium bowl. Add chicken and toss to coat. Place chicken on prepared pan and broil, turning once, until cooked through, about 3 minutes per side.

2 Meanwhile, to make slaw, combine yogurt, mayonnaise, cilantro, lime juice, and remaining ⅛ teaspoon salt in large bowl. Add coleslaw mix and radishes; toss to coat.

3 Layer each lavash with ¼ cup slaw, one-fourth of chicken, and ⅓ cup salad greens. Roll up and cut each wrap in half. Serve remaining slaw on the side.

Per serving (2 sandwich halves and ¼ cup slaw): 264 Cal, 4 g Total Fat, 1 g Sat Fat, 0 g Trans Fat, 47 mg Chol, 419 mg Sod, 30 g Carb, 1 g Sugar, 4 g Fib, 23 g Prot, 69 mg Calc.

For Your Information

Can't find chicken tenders? Cut one large (¾-pound) skin-less boneless chicken breast lengthwise into eight equal strips and prepare the recipe as directed.

wild salmon burgers with cucumber salsa
SERVES 4

- 1 pound skinless wild salmon fillet, finely diced
- 1 small shallot, finely chopped
- ½ teaspoon Dijon mustard
- ¼ teaspoon black pepper
- 2 tablespoons chopped fresh cilantro
- ¼ teaspoon salt
- 1 cup diced English (seedless) cucumber
- Juice of ½ lime
- ¼ teaspoon jalapeño pepper sauce
- 1 cup watercress leaves
- 4 multigrain English muffins, split and toasted

1 Combine salmon, shallot, mustard, black pepper, 1 tablespoon cilantro, and ⅛ teaspoon salt in medium bowl; mix to combine. Form into 4 patties, each about ½-inch thick. Spray large nonstick skillet with nonstick spray and set over medium heat. Add patties and cook until lightly browned and cooked through, 5–6 minutes per side.

2 Meanwhile, to make salsa, combine cucumber, lime juice, pepper sauce, remaining 1 tablespoon cilantro, and remaining ⅛ teaspoon salt in medium bowl.

3 Layer ¼ cup watercress, burger, and ⅓ cup salsa into each English muffin.

Per serving (1 burger): 345 Cal, 10 g Total Fat, 1 g Sat Fat, 0 g Trans Fat, 72 mg Chol, 392 mg Sod, 35 g Carb, 5 g Sugar, 4 g Fib, 31 g Prot, 182 mg Calc.

For Your Information
Before you dice the salmon in step 1, it's best to run your fingers over the fillet and feel for any small pin bones. If you feel any, use tweezers or needle-nose pliers to pull them out (or ask your fishmonger to remove any bones for you).

grilled tofu pita burgers

SERVES 4

1 tablespoon olive oil

1 ½ teaspoons red-wine vinegar

1 garlic clove, minced

¼ teaspoon black pepper

▲ 1 (14-ounce) container low-fat firm tofu, cut crosswise into 4 slices

4 (7-inch) whole wheat pocketless pitas

⅓ cup prepared hummus

▲ 2 cups baby arugula

▲ 4 slices tomato

▲ 4 thin slices red onion

2 teaspoons Sriracha or other chili sauce

1 Combine oil, vinegar, garlic, and pepper in shallow dish; add tofu in single layer. Let stand 30 minutes, turning tofu after 15 minutes.

2 Drain tofu. Spray ridged grill pan with nonstick spray and set over medium-high heat until very hot. Place tofu in pan and grill until evenly browned, about 4 minutes per side.

3 Top pitas evenly with hummus, arugula, tomato, tofu, onion, and Sriracha. Serve at once.

Per serving (1 sandwich): 299 Cal, 9 g Total Fat, 1 g Sat Fat, 0 g Trans Fat, 0 mg Chol, 522 mg Sod, 42 g Carb, 2 g Sugar, 7 g Fib, 17 g Prot, 222 mg Calc.

Make Ahead

You can prepare the tofu as directed in step 1, then cover it and let it marinate in the refrigerator, turning occasionally, up to 24 hours. This will allow the tofu to absorb more of the marinade and become even more flavorful.

skip-the-meat muffuletta
SERVES 8

- ▲ 1 small (½-pound) eggplant, cut lengthwise into ¾-inch slices

- ⅛ teaspoon salt

- ½ cup fresh basil leaves

- 1 cup part-skim ricotta cheese

- 1 small garlic clove, minced

- ¼ teaspoon black pepper

- ▲ 1 cup jarred roasted red bell peppers (not packed in oil), drained

- ▲ 1 cup canned artichoke hearts in brine, drained

- ¼ cup brine-cured pitted black olives, chopped

- ▲ 1 tomato, sliced

- 1 (7-inch) round whole wheat crusty bread

1 Sprinkle eggplant with salt. Spray ridged grill pan with nonstick spray and set over medium-high heat until very hot. Place eggplant in pan and grill until browned and tender, 4–5 minutes per side. Transfer eggplant to plate.

2 Chop enough basil to equal 1 tablespoon. Combine chopped basil, ricotta, garlic, and black pepper in medium bowl. Pat roasted peppers and artichokes dry with paper towels.

3 Cut ¾-inch slice from top of bread for lid. Remove soft center from lid and loaf, leaving ½-inch-thick shell. Discard soft center (or save for bread crumbs). Layer half of roasted peppers, half of artichokes, eggplant, olives, tomato, remaining basil, and half of ricotta mixture in bread shell. Repeat with remaining roasted peppers, remaining artichokes, and remaining ricotta mixture. Cover with lid and wrap tightly in plastic wrap. Refrigerate 8 hours or overnight.

4 To serve, unwrap loaf and cut into 8 wedges.

Per serving (1 wedge): 190 Cal, 5 g Total Fat, 2 g Sat Fat, 0 g Trans Fat, 10 mg Chol, 500 mg Sod, 28 g Carb, 3 g Sugar, 4 g Fib, 9 g Prot, 101 mg Calc.

Make Ahead
This sandwich is based on the New Orleans classic, but replaces the traditional deli meats with creamy ricotta cheese. It should be refrigerated at least 8 hours to soften, but you can actually assemble it up to 2 days before serving.

POT O' PUMPKIN SOUP WITH MAPLE BACON p 38
SKIP-THE-MEAT MUFFULETTA p 35

pot o' pumpkin soup with maple bacon

SERVES 4

½ teaspoon olive oil

3 strips maple-smoked bacon, chopped

1 onion, chopped

2 garlic cloves, finely chopped

2 celery stalks, chopped

1 large apple, cored and chopped

1 (14-ounce) can pumpkin puree

½ cup quick-cooking oats

3 cups reduced-sodium chicken broth

½ teaspoon salt

¼ teaspoon black pepper

1 teaspoon apple cider vinegar

Chives for garnish

1 Heat oil in medium pot over medium heat. Add bacon; cook, stirring, until golden brown and crisp, about 5 minutes. Transfer bacon to paper towels to drain.

2 Return pot to medium heat and add onion, garlic, celery, and apple. Cook, stirring, until celery softens, about 5 minutes. Add pumpkin puree, oats, broth, salt, and pepper; bring to boil. Reduce heat to medium-low and simmer until oats are very tender, about 10 minutes. Stir in vinegar.

3 Let soup cool 5 minutes. Working in batches, puree soup in blender or food processor. Serve garnished with chives and reserved bacon.

Per serving (1 ¾ cups soup and 1 tablespoon bacon):
170 Cal, 5 g Total Fat, 1 g Sat Fat, 0 g Trans Fat, 5 mg Chol, 489 mg Sod, 26 g Carb, 10 g Sugar, 7 g Fib, 9 g Prot, 57 mg Calc.

For Your Information

Make sure you use pure pumpkin puree and not pumpkin pie filling for the soup. While both contain pumpkin, the latter is loaded with sugar. You can substitute a thawed box of frozen cooked winter squash.

slow-cooker beef and barley soup with rosemary

SERVES 6

Ingredients

- 1 onion, diced
- 3 garlic cloves, finely chopped
- 3 carrots, chopped
- Leaves from 4 sprigs fresh rosemary, chopped
- 2 teaspoons Worcestershire sauce
- 3 cups reduced-sodium beef broth
- 3 cups low-sodium tomato juice
- 3 cups water
- ¾ cup pearl barley
- ¼ teaspoon black pepper
- 1 pound lean beef bottom round ("pot roast" cut), trimmed and cut into 1-inch-thick slices
- 1 (10-ounce) box frozen chopped spinach, thawed

1 Combine onion, garlic, carrots, rosemary, Worcestershire sauce, broth, tomato juice, water, barley, and pepper in slow cooker. Add beef. Cover and cook until barley and beef are tender, 4–5 hours on high or 8–10 hours on low.

2 With tongs, remove beef slices from slow cooker. Using two forks, shred beef; then return it to pot. Add spinach and cook on high until heated through, about 10 minutes.

Per serving (1 ½ cups): 292 Cal, 6 g Total Fat, 2 g Sat Fat, 0 g Trans Fat, 59 mg Chol, 230 mg Sod, 33 g Carb, 9 g Sugar, 8 g Fib, 27 g Prot, 114 mg Calc.

For Your Information

To maximize the nutrients you get from root vegetables like carrots and potatoes, leave the skin on. Buy organic when you can to avoid the pesticides that can accumulate in the skins of conventionally grown produce.

STORING LEFTOVERS EASILY AND SAFELY

Having leftovers on hand is a welcome benefit of cooking at home, and some foods, like stews and casseroles, are even better the next time around! Keep these rules in mind to ensure that your food is wonderfully delicious for another day. See Cozy Up to Freezing (page 170) for specific information on freezing leftovers and other foods.

Speed cooling. Many foods are at risk for bacterial growth if they cool too slowly. To safely store soups and stews, transfer them to several smaller containers, and allow them to stand at room temperature until cooled, no longer than two hours, and then refrigerate or freeze immediately. Alternatively, place a larger container of food in an ice bath to cool it more quickly.

Portion out foods. If you'll be reheating a dish for a family meal, you can store the food in one large container. But if you anticipate reheating just enough for one or two people, it will be more convenient to divide it into single-serving portions before storing.

Label accurately. Mark your leftovers with the name of the dish, the serving size, the *PointsPlus* value, and the date. This will simplify your tracking, and also help you keep tabs on when to use foods for best quality. Use an indelible marker; freezer tape, which is especially designed to adhere in moist conditions, is also useful.

Cover and seal. Leave as little air in the container as possible for best storage results. If you're freezing liquid foods like soups or stews, however, leave some headspace at the top of the container since these foods will expand slightly during the freezing process.

Keep baked goods fresh. Cool baked goods completely before storing. Small items like muffins and scones can be placed in airtight containers or small zip-close plastic freezer bags. Larger items like loaves of bread or cakes can be wrapped tightly in plastic wrap, then in foil. The quality of baked goods decreases rapidly at room temperature, and most do not refrigerate well, so plan to freeze what you won't eat right away. Added bonus: Getting it out of sight means you won't be tempted to snack on impulse. See page 170 for more freezing tips.

RECOMMENDED STORAGE TIMES
FOR COOKED FOODS

Use the chart below to determine how long to keep leftovers in the refrigerator or freezer. While frozen foods can remain safe almost indefinitely, follow these recommended times to ensure the best quality and flavor.

TYPE OF LEFTOVER	REFRIGERATED	FROZEN
BEEF, PORK, LAMB	3-4 days	2-3 months
POULTRY	3-4 days	4 months
SEAFOOD	2-3 days	2-3 months
EGG DISHES	3-4 days	not recommended
SOUPS, STEWS, CASSEROLES	3-4 days	2-3 months
BAKED GOODS	not recommended	2-3 months
FRUIT AND DAIRY DESSERTS	4-5 days	not recommended

slow-cooker georgia garden gumbo soup

SERVES 6

- ▲ **4 cups reduced-sodium chicken broth**
- ▲ **1 cup brown rice**
- **4 ounces Cajun-flavored or spicy chicken sausage, sliced**
- ▲ **1 large onion, chopped**
- ▲ **1 large red bell pepper, chopped**
- ▲ **3 celery stalks, chopped**
- **2 teaspoons dried thyme**
- **2 teaspoons sweet paprika**
- **2 teaspoons Worcestershire sauce**
- **1 teaspoon hot pepper sauce**
- **¼ teaspoon salt**
- ▲ **1 (10-ounce) box frozen sliced okra, thawed**
- **Zest of 1 lemon**
- **¼ cup chopped fresh parsley**

1 Combine broth, rice, sausage, onion, bell pepper, celery, thyme, paprika, Worcestershire sauce, pepper sauce, and salt in slow cooker. Cover and cook until rice and vegetables are very tender, 4–5 hours on high or 8–10 hours on low.

2 Stir in okra and zest; cook on high until heated through, about 10 minutes. Sprinkle with parsley.

Per serving (1 generous cup): 207 Cal, 3 g Total Fat, 1 g Sat Fat, 0 g Trans Fat, 15 mg Chol, 348 mg Sod, 36 g Carb, 4 g Sugar, 5 g Fib, 11 g Prot, 95 mg Calc.

For Your Information

If you like spicy food, go ahead and pour on the hot sauce! Look for one that is low in sodium, and you can indulge in as much fiery flavor as you want.

fiery thai salmon soup

SERVES 4

1½ teaspoons peanut oil

▲ 1 small onion, thinly sliced

▲ 1 large carrot, thinly sliced

2 teaspoons prepared green curry paste

2 teaspoons Sriracha or other hot pepper sauce

1 (14-ounce) can light (reduced-fat) coconut milk

▲ 2 cups reduced-sodium vegetable broth

1 tablespoon reduced-sodium soy sauce

▲ 1 (6-ounce) piece wild salmon fillet, skin removed, cut into ¾-inch pieces

▲ 1 cup frozen peas, thawed

▲ 1 (8-ounce) can bamboo shoots, drained

¼ cup chopped fresh cilantro

1 Heat oil in medium pot over medium heat. Add onion, carrot, and curry paste. Cook, stirring, until vegetables soften, about 5 minutes.

2 Add Sriracha, coconut milk, broth, and soy sauce; bring to boil. Reduce heat to medium-low and add salmon, peas, and bamboo shoots. Simmer, stirring occasionally, until salmon is cooked through, about 5 minutes. Sprinkle with cilantro.

Per serving (1 ½ cups): 215 Cal, 12 g Total Fat, 1 g Sat Fat, 0 g Trans Fat, 27 mg Chol, 326 mg Sod, 17 g Carb, 5 g Sugar, 4 g Fib, 14 g Prot, 38 mg Calc.

Stay On Track

For more veggie flavor, add a diced red bell pepper to the soup along with the carrot.

smoky shrimp and corn chowder
SERVES 4

- 2 teaspoons peanut oil
- ▲ 1 large red onion, diced
- ▲ 2 celery stalks, thinly sliced
- 2 tablespoons all-purpose flour
- ¾ teaspoon smoked paprika
- ▲ 2 cups fat-free half-and-half
- ▲ 1 ½ cups fresh or frozen thawed corn kernels
- ¼ teaspoon salt
- ▲ ½ pound medium shrimp, peeled and deveined
- ▲ 2 scallions, thinly sliced

1 Heat oil in large saucepan over medium heat. Add onion and celery. Cook, stirring occasionally, until vegetables soften, about 5 minutes. Add flour and paprika, and cook, stirring constantly, 1 minute.

2 Remove saucepan from heat. Add half-and-half, whisking until smooth. Add corn and salt. Cook over medium heat, stirring constantly, until chowder thickens, about 3 minutes.

3 Add shrimp and cook, stirring frequently, until shrimp are just opaque in center, about 3 minutes. Sprinkle chowder with scallions.

Per serving (1 ¼ cups): 228 Cal, 4 g Total Fat, 1 g Sat Fat, 0 g Trans Fat, 84 mg Chol, 378 mg Sod, 31 g Carb, 12 g Sugar, 3 g Fib, 16 g Prot, 201 mg Calc.

Stay On Track
Make this chowder a filling meal-in-a-bowl by adding 1 cup cooked wild rice along with the corn, increasing the per-serving *PointsPlus* value by *1.*

broccoli-cauliflower soup with fontina

SERVES 4

2 teaspoons olive oil

▲ 1 small leek, sliced and rinsed

1 garlic clove, finely chopped

2 tablespoons all-purpose flour

▲ 2 cups fat-free milk

▲ 1 ½ cups reduced-sodium chicken or vegetable broth

▲ 1 large head broccoli, stem peeled and chopped, crowns chopped

▲ ¼ head cauliflower, chopped

▲ ½ cup canned white beans, rinsed and drained

1 teaspoon Dijon mustard

½ teaspoon black pepper

½ cup shredded fontina cheese

1 Heat oil in large saucepan over medium heat. Add leek and garlic; cook, stirring, until softened, about 5 minutes. Add flour, and cook, stirring, 1 minute. Slowly stir in milk and broth; bring to boil, stirring frequently.

2 Add broccoli, cauliflower, beans, mustard, and pepper. Simmer, stirring occasionally, until vegetables are very tender, about 10 minutes.

3 Remove soup from heat and let cool 5 minutes. Working in batches, puree soup in blender or food processor. Stir ¼ cup fontina cheese into soup, and reheat if necessary. Serve garnished with remaining cheese.

Per serving (1 ½ cups soup and 1 tablespoon cheese): 239 Cal, 8 g Total Fat, 3 g Sat Fat, 0 g Trans Fat, 18 mg Chol, 356 mg Sod, 29 g Carb, 10 g Sugar, 6 g Fib, 16 g Prot, 334 mg Calc.

For Your Information

Use caution when blending hot liquids: Their heat can cause the air in the blender to expand, sometimes explosively enough to blow the lid off and send scalding liquid all over your kitchen. Play it safe by never filling the container more than half full. Hold the lid down gently with a folded kitchen towel, and start the blender on low speed, never high.

RED, WHITE, AND GREEN MINESTRONE

red, white, and green minestrone

SERVES 4

2 teaspoons olive oil

▲ 1 onion, chopped

2 teaspoons chopped fresh rosemary

▲ 1 (14-ounce) can no-salt-added cannellini (white kidney) beans, rinsed and drained

▲ 1 (14-ounce) can no-salt-added diced tomatoes

▲ 3 cups reduced-sodium chicken or vegetable broth

¼ teaspoon salt

¼ teaspoon black pepper

▲ 1 bunch kale, stems and tough ribs removed, leaves chopped

3 ounces spinach fettuccine, broken into 2-inch pieces (about ¾ cup)

2 tablespoons grated Parmesan cheese

4 teaspoons prepared pesto

1 Heat oil in large saucepan over medium heat. Add onion and rosemary; cook, stirring, until onion softens, about 5 minutes.

2 Add beans, tomatoes, broth, salt, and pepper; bring to boil. Stir in kale and fettuccine; return to boil. Cover, reduce heat, and cook, stirring occasionally, until pasta and kale are tender, about 12 minutes. Serve soup garnished with Parmesan cheese and pesto.

Per serving (1 ¾ cups soup, ½ tablespoon cheese, and 1 teaspoon pesto): 290 Cal, 8 g Total Fat, 2 g Sat Fat, 0 g Trans Fat, 4 mg Chol, 351 mg Sod, 43 g Carb, 7 g Sugar, 7 g Fib, 15 g Prot, 173 mg Calc.

Make Ahead

This is a terrific soup to refrigerate up to 4 days or to freeze in single-serving portions for up to 3 months. You can stir the cheese and pesto into the soup before storing, or add it as a garnish just before serving.

tomato-basil lentil soup

SERVES 4

- 2 teaspoons olive oil
- ▲ 1 small onion, finely chopped
- 1 clove garlic, finely chopped
- ▲ 1 cup brown lentils, rinsed and picked over
- ▲ 1 (28-ounce) can no-salt-added crushed tomatoes
- ▲ 2 ½ cups reduced-sodium chicken or vegetable broth
- 3 sprigs fresh basil, stems and leaves reserved separately
- ½ teaspoon salt
- ¼ teaspoon black pepper
- ▲ 2 tablespoons fat-free half-and-half

1 Heat oil in large saucepan over medium heat. Add onion and garlic; cook, stirring, until softened, about 5 minutes.

2 Add lentils, tomatoes, broth, basil stems, salt, and pepper; bring to boil. Simmer, stirring occasionally, until lentils are tender, 15–20 minutes.

3 Remove and discard basil stems. Stir in half-and-half. Tear basil leaves into pieces and sprinkle over soup.

Per serving (1 ¾ cups): 265 Cal, 4 g Total Fat, 1 g Sat Fat. 0 g Trans Fat, 0 mg Chol, 369 mg Sod, 42 g Carb, 10 g Sugar, 13 g Fib, 18 g Prot, 83 mg Calc.

For Your Information

The stems of the basil plant may not be as palatable as the leaves, but they're still packed with flavor. Add them to soups and stews or to boiling water for corn for extra basil flavor—just don't forget to remove them before serving!

chilled beet and yogurt soup

SERVES 4

- ▲ **1 pound beets, trimmed and scrubbed**
- ▲ **1 small onion, halved**
- **4 cups water**
- **1 tablespoon sugar**
- **1 tablespoon lemon juice**
- **½ teaspoon salt**
- **Pinch cayenne**
- ▲ **⅔ cup plain fat-free Greek yogurt**
- ▲ **1 Kirby cucumber, peeled and diced**
- ▲ **2 scallions, thinly sliced**
- **¼ cup chopped fresh dill**

1 Combine beets, onion, and water in large saucepan; bring to boil. Reduce heat and simmer, covered, until beets are tender, about 40 minutes.

2 Set large fine-mesh sieve over large bowl. Pour beet mixture into sieve; discard onion and reserve liquid. When beets are cool enough to handle, slip off skin. Cut half of beets into quarters, then puree with beet liquid in food processor or blender. Transfer to large bowl. Coarsely grate remaining beets and add to bowl. Stir in sugar, lemon juice, salt, and cayenne. Cover and refrigerate until well chilled, at least 4 hours or up to overnight.

3 Whisk in yogurt just before serving. Ladle soup into 4 bowls and top evenly with cucumber, scallions, and dill.

Per serving (about 1 cup): 92 Cal, 0 g Total Fat, 0 g Sat Fat, 0 g Trans Fat, 0 mg Chol, 401 mg Sod, 18 g Carb, 14 g Sugar, 3 g Fib, 6 g Prot, 67 mg Calc.

Stay On Track
Serve this soup with tasty rye toast; 1 slice reduced-calorie rye bread per person will increase the per-serving *PointsPlus* value by **2.**

beefed-up tabbouleh salad

SERVES 4

1 cup bulgur

1 cup boiling water

Grated zest and juice of ½ lemon

4 (¼-pound) pieces lean tri-tip steak, trimmed

½ teaspoon salt

½ teaspoon black pepper

2 teaspoons olive oil

2 teaspoons coarse-grained mustard

1 cucumber, peeled, seeded, and diced

1 pint cherry tomatoes, halved

⅓ cup fresh mint leaves, chopped

2 scallions, thinly sliced

1 Combine bulgur, boiling water, and lemon juice in medium bowl. Stir once, cover bowl, and let stand until liquid is absorbed, about 30 minutes.

2 Meanwhile, sprinkle steaks with ¼ teaspoon salt and ¼ teaspoon pepper. Spray ridged grill pan with nonstick spray and set over medium-high heat until very hot. Place steaks in pan and grill until instant-read thermometer inserted into side of each steak registers 145°F for medium-rare, 6–7 minutes per side. Transfer steaks to cutting board and let stand 5 minutes.

3 Combine oil, mustard, lemon zest, remaining ¼ teaspoon salt, and remaining ¼ teaspoon pepper in large bowl. Stir in bulgur mixture, cucumber, tomatoes, mint, and scallions. Thinly slice steaks across grain and serve with salad.

Per serving (1 steak and 1¼ cups salad): 321 Cal, 10 g Total Fat, 3 g Sat Fat, 0 g Trans Fat, 60 mg Chol, 385 mg Sod, 32 g Carb, 3 g Sugar, 8 g Fib, 28 g Prot, 57 mg Calc.

marinated cherry salad with rosemary ham

SERVES 4

¼ cup balsamic vinegar

1 ½ teaspoons packed brown sugar

▲ ¾ pound fresh sweet cherries, pitted

½ teaspoon chopped fresh thyme

4 teaspoons walnut or olive oil

¼ teaspoon black pepper

▲ ½ fennel bulb, thinly sliced

1 (6-ounce) package sliced rosemary ham, cut into strips

▲ 1 (5-ounce) bag mixed baby greens

1 Combine vinegar and sugar in small saucepan and set over medium heat; bring to boil. Reduce heat and simmer until mixture reduces by half, about 2 minutes. Transfer to medium bowl and stir in cherries and thyme. Cover and refrigerate, stirring occasionally, until flavors are blended, at least 30 minutes or overnight.

2 Drain cherries in sieve set over medium bowl; set aside (see below) all but 1½ teaspoons soaking liquid.

3 Whisk oil, reserved liquid, and pepper in large bowl. Add cherries, fennel, ham, and greens; toss to coat.

Per serving (2 ¾ cups): 164 Cal, 6 g Total Fat, 1 g Sat Fat, 0 g Trans Fat, 16 mg Chol, 486 mg Sod, 20 g Carb, 15 g Sugar, 4 g Fib, 8 g Prot, 28 mg Calc.

For Your Information

Save the liquid the cherries soaked in, and refrigerate it up to 1 week. You can use it in place of vinegar for other salads. You should have about ½ cup.

kale caesar salad with grilled chicken

SERVES 4

1 teaspoon canola oil

⅛ teaspoon salt

½ teaspoon black pepper

▲ 1 pound chicken breast tenders

3 tablespoons low-fat buttermilk

2 tablespoons low-fat mayonnaise

2 tablespoons grated Parmesan cheese

1 small garlic clove, minced

¼ teaspoon anchovy paste

▲ 1 (5-ounce) package baby kale

1½ cups fat-free croutons

▲ ½ small red onion, thinly sliced

1 Combine oil, salt, and ¼ teaspoon pepper in medium bowl. Add chicken and toss to coat. Set ridged grill pan over medium-high heat until very hot. Place chicken in pan and grill until cooked through, 3–4 minutes per side. Transfer chicken to cutting board. When cool enough to handle, cut chicken into 1½-inch pieces.

2 Meanwhile, to make dressing, whisk together buttermilk, mayonnaise, Parmesan, garlic, anchovy paste, and remaining ¼ teaspoon pepper in large bowl.

3 Add chicken, kale, croutons, and onion to dressing and toss to coat.

Per serving (2 ¾ cups): 215 Cal, 6 g Total Fat, 2 g Sat Fat, 0 g Trans Fat, 66 mg Chol, 410 mg Sod, 14 g Carb, 1 g Sugar, 1 g Fib, 27 g Prot, 105 mg Calc.

provençal-style tuna and potato salad

SERVES 4

- **1 pound small red potatoes, scrubbed and halved**
- **¼ pound green beans, trimmed and cut into 1-inch pieces**
- **3 tablespoons reduced-sodium chicken broth**
- **2 tablespoons red-wine vinegar**
- **1 tablespoon Dijon mustard**
- **2 teaspoons olive oil**
- **¼ teaspoon salt**
- **½ teaspoon black pepper**
- **1 (5-ounce) can reduced-sodium chunk light tuna in water, drained**
- **1 cup grape tomatoes, halved**
- **3 scallions, sliced**
- **1 tablespoon capers, rinsed and drained**
- **3 tablespoons chopped fresh parsley**

1 Place potatoes in medium saucepan with enough water to cover by 1 inch; bring to boil. Cook 10 minutes. Add green beans and cook until potatoes and green beans are tender, 4–5 minutes longer. Drain.

2 Meanwhile, to make dressing, combine broth, vinegar, mustard, oil, salt, and pepper in large bowl; whisk until blended.

3 Add potatoes and green beans to dressing; toss to coat. Add tuna, tomatoes, scallions, capers, and parsley; toss again. Serve warm or chilled.

Per serving (1 ¼ cups): 165 Cal, 3 g Total Fat, 0 g Sat Fat, 0 g Trans Fat, 19 mg Chol, 473 mg Sod, 24 g Carb, 3 g Sugar, 4 g Fib, 12 g Prot, 41 mg Calc.

Make Ahead
This meal in a bowl makes a terrific pack-along. It will keep stored in an airtight container and refrigerated up to 3 days.

red curry noodle salad

SERVES 4

- ▲ **6 ounces brown rice stick noodles**
- **Juice of 1 lime**
- **1 tablespoon reduced-sodium soy sauce**
- **1 ½ teaspoons Asian fish sauce**
- **1 ½ teaspoons mirin**
- **1 ½ teaspoons packed brown sugar**
- **¼ teaspoon Thai red curry paste**
- ▲ **2 carrots, cut into matchstick strips**
- ▲ **4 radishes, cut into matchstick strips**
- **⅓ cup fresh cilantro leaves**
- **⅓ cup fresh mint leaves**
- ▲ **4 large hard-cooked eggs, peeled and sliced**
- **4 teaspoons unsalted dry-roasted peanuts, coarsely chopped**

1 Bring large pot of water to boil. Add noodles and cook, stirring frequently, just until tender, about 2 minutes. Drain in colander and rinse with cold water. Drain again.

2 Meanwhile, to make dressing, whisk together lime juice, soy sauce, fish sauce, mirin, brown sugar, and curry paste in large bowl until blended.

3 Add noodles, carrots, radishes, cilantro, and mint to dressing; toss to coat. Divide salad evenly among 4 plates. Top each salad with 1 egg and 1 teaspoon peanuts.

Per serving (generous 1 cup noodle mixture, 1 egg, and 1 teaspoon peanuts): 276 Cal, 7 g Total Fat, 2 g Sat Fat, 0 g Trans Fat, 212 mg Chol, 407 mg Sod, 45 g Carb, 5 g Sugar, 2 g Fib, 8 g Prot, 59 mg Calc.

Stay On Track

For more crunch, add a cup of nutrient-packed mung bean sprouts to the salad along with the carrots and radishes in step 3.

RED CURRY NOODLE SALAD

green goddess chicken salad

⅓ cup part-skim ricotta cheese

¼ cup low-fat buttermilk

▲ 2 scallions, chopped

3 tablespoons fresh parsley leaves

1 tablespoon chopped fresh dill

1 tablespoon fresh tarragon leaves

2 teaspoons low-fat mayonnaise

½ garlic clove, minced

½ teaspoon anchovy paste

½ teaspoon salt

Pinch cayenne

▲ 2 cups diced cooked skinless chicken breast

▲ 2 celery stalks, diced

▲ 4 Boston lettuce leaves

1 To make dressing, puree ricotta, buttermilk, scallions, parsley, dill, tarragon, mayonnaise, garlic, anchovy paste, salt, and cayenne in blender.

2 Transfer dressing to large bowl. Add chicken and celery, and toss to coat. Line platter with lettuce leaves and top with chicken salad.

Per serving (¾ cup salad and 1 lettuce leaf): 165 Cal, 5 g Total Fat, 2 g Sat Fat, 0 g Trans Fat, 69 mg Chol, 477 mg Sod, 4 g Carb, 2 g Sugar, 1 g Fib, 25 g Prot, 110 mg Calc.

Stay On Track

Serve this elegant salad with a side of peeled sliced cantaloupe.

mexi cobb salad with spicy pepitas
SERVES 4

½ teaspoon canola oil

2 tablespoons raw unsalted pepitas (green pumpkin seeds)

½ teaspoon Mexican or Southwest seasoning blend

3 slices turkey bacon

▲ ¾ pound thin-sliced skinless turkey breast cutlets

¼ teaspoon black pepper

▲ 8 cups shredded romaine lettuce

▲ 1 large tomato, diced

▲ ½ small red onion, diced

½ cup crumbled Cotija or low-fat feta cheese

¼ cup low-fat vinaigrette dressing

1 Heat oil in large nonstick skillet over medium heat. Add pepitas and seasoning blend. Cook, stirring occasionally, until pepitas are lightly browned, about 2 minutes. With slotted spoon, transfer pepitas to plate and let cool.

2 Return skillet to medium heat. Add bacon and cook, turning occasionally, until browned, 4–5 minutes. Transfer to cutting board and dice.

3 Sprinkle turkey with pepper. Spray skillet with nonstick spray and set over medium heat. Add turkey and cook until cooked through, about 3–4 minutes per side. Transfer turkey to cutting board. When cool enough to handle, dice turkey.

4 Line large platter with lettuce. Place turkey, tomato, onion, Cotija cheese, and bacon in stripes over lettuce. Sprinkle evenly with pepitas. Serve drizzled with dressing.

Per serving (3 ¾ cups salad and 1 tablespoon dressing):
242 Cal, 10 g Total Fat, 3 g Sat Fat, 0 g Trans Fat, 49 mg Chol, 770 mg Sod, 11 g Carb, 4 g Sugar, 3 g Fib, 31 g Prot, 91 mg Calc.

For Your Information
Pepitas have a lovely nutty flavor and tender bite, and they're packed with nutrition. Look for them in larger supermarkets, Hispanic grocery stores, or health-food stores. You can also substitute an equal amount of shelled sunflower seeds.

mediterranean fava bean salad

SERVES 4

- ▲ **2 cups frozen shelled fava beans or edamame**
- **1 tablespoon red-wine vinegar**
- **2 teaspoons olive oil**
- **1 teaspoon Dijon mustard**
- **1 shallot, finely chopped**
- **¼ teaspoon salt**
- **⅛ teaspoon red pepper flakes**
- ▲ **1 small fennel bulb, trimmed and thinly sliced**
- ▲ **1 tomato, chopped**
- **¼ cup pitted brine-cured niçoise olives, halved**
- **¼ cup chopped fresh parsley**

1 Bring water filling two-thirds of medium saucepan to boil over medium-high heat; stir in beans. Cook until tender, about 8 minutes. Drain in colander; rinse under cold running water and drain again. Peel off thick outer skins from fava beans if necessary; discard skins.

2 Combine vinegar, oil, mustard, shallot, salt, and pepper flakes in large bowl; whisk until blended. Add beans, fennel, tomato, olives, and parsley to bowl; toss to coat.

Per serving (1 cup): 142 Cal, 6 g Total Fat, 0 g Sat Fat, 0 g Trans Fat, 0 mg Chol, 315 mg Sod, 16 g Carb, 3 g Sugar, 7 g Fib, 8 g Prot, 105 mg Calc.

For Your Information

Fava beans are often frozen with their tough, whitish outer skin intact. You can remove the skin by piercing one end with your fingernail and then slipping the bean out.

wheat berry salad with citrus and mint

SERVES 4

- ▲ **1 cup wheat berries**
- ▲ **2 navel oranges**
- ▲ **1 large red grapefruit**
- **2 tablespoons rice vinegar**
- **2 teaspoons olive oil**
- ▲ **1 cup canned no-salt-added chickpeas, rinsed and drained**
- ▲ **½ cup diced red onion**
- **¼ cup chopped fresh mint**
- **1 garlic clove, minced**
- **¼ teaspoon salt**

1 Bring water filling two-thirds of medium saucepan to boil over high heat; stir in wheat berries. Reduce heat and simmer, covered, until berries are tender but still chewy, about 1 hour. Drain and rinse under cold running water; drain again.

2 Meanwhile, remove zest from 1 orange and set aside. With small knife, cut away skin and white pith from oranges and grapefruit. Working over small bowl, cut between membranes to release segments. Squeeze juice from membranes. Transfer citrus segments to large bowl, leaving juice in small bowl. Whisk vinegar, oil, and reserved orange zest into juice.

3 Add wheat berries, chickpeas, onion, mint, garlic, and salt to citrus segments. Drizzle with juice mixture and toss to coat.

Per serving (1 ¼ cups): 326 Cal, 4 g Total Fat, 0 g Sat Fat, 0 g Trans Fat, 0 mg Chol, 164 mg Sod, 62 g Carb, 14 g Sugar, 10 g Fib, 12 g Prot, 95 mg Calc.

Make Ahead

If you like, prepare a double batch of the wheat berries, so you'll have them on hand to make this delicious salad another day. They'll keep refrigerated up to 4 days or frozen up to 3 months.

Chapter 3

one-pot stews & skillet favorites

one-pot stews & skillet favorites

tex-mex brisket

1 (2-pound) lean beef brisket, trimmed

2 teaspoons ground cumin

1 teaspoon chipotle chile powder

¼ teaspoon salt

½ teaspoon black pepper

▲ 1 Vidalia or other sweet onion, chopped

3 garlic cloves, finely chopped

1 (12-ounce) jar chili sauce

1 (12-ounce) can light beer

1 small avocado, pitted, peeled, and diced

▲ 1 small red onion, sliced

1 Preheat oven to 325°F. Sprinkle beef with cumin, chile powder, salt, and pepper. Spray large Dutch oven with nonstick spray and set over medium-high heat. Add beef and cook until browned, about 4 minutes per side. Transfer beef to plate.

2 Spray Dutch oven again with nonstick spray; return to medium heat. Add onion and cook, covered, stirring occasionally, until tender, about 5 minutes. Add garlic and cook, stirring frequently, until fragrant, about 30 seconds. Stir in chili sauce and beer; add beef. Bring to boil. Cover and bake until beef is fork-tender, 2½–3 hours.

3 Transfer beef to cutting board. Cut beef across grain on diagonal into 16 thin slices and place on platter. Top with 1 cup sauce, avocado, and red onion. Serve remaining sauce on side.

Per serving (2 slices brisket, ¼ cup avocado and onion, and ¼ cup sauce): 273 Cal, 7 g Total Fat, 2 g Sat Fat, 0 g Trans Fat, 59 mg Chol, 705 mg Sod, 19 g Carb, 10 g Sugar, 1 g Fib, 29 g Prot, 34 mg Calc.

Make Ahead
This dish freezes beautifully. Transfer sliced brisket to a large freezer-safe container. Add sauce and let cool to room temperature; then cover and freeze. To serve, thaw overnight in the refrigerator and reheat in a Dutch oven over medium-low heat. Garnish with avocado and onion.

slow-cooker tropical pot roast

SERVES 8

- ▲ 1 (2-pound) lean boneless beef bottom round roast, trimmed
- 2 teaspoons chili powder
- 1 teaspoon salt
- ½ teaspoon black pepper
- ⅛ teaspoon cinnamon
- 1 teaspoon canola oil
- ▲ 1 large red onion, sliced
- 3 garlic cloves, finely chopped
- ⅔ cup tequila
- ▲ 1 (14 ½-ounce) can no-salt-added diced tomatoes
- ▲ 1 cup reduced-sodium chicken broth
- ▲ ½ cup chopped fresh pineapple
- ¼ cup lime juice
- 1 chipotle en adobo, chopped

1 Sprinkle beef with chili powder, salt, pepper, and cinnamon. Spray large heavy skillet with nonstick spray and set over medium-high heat. Add beef and cook, turning occasionally, until browned on all sides, 10–12 minutes. Transfer beef to 5- or 6-quart slow cooker.

2 Return skillet to medium heat and add oil. Add onion and cook, covered, stirring occasionally, until tender, 3–4 minutes. Add garlic and cook, stirring frequently, until fragrant, about 30 seconds. Stir in tequila and bring to boil, scraping any browned bits from bottom of pan with spoon. Boil until reduced by half, 2–3 minutes. Pour tequila mixture over beef.

3 Add tomatoes, broth, pineapple, lime juice, and chipotle to slow cooker. Cover and cook until beef is fork-tender, 5–6 hours on high or 10–12 hours on low. Transfer beef to cutting board. Cut beef across grain on diagonal into 16 thin slices; serve with sauce.

Per serving (2 slices beef and ⅓ cup sauce): 261 Cal, 7 g Total Fat, 2 g Sat Fat, 0 g Trans Fat, 88 mg Chol, 357 mg Sod, 8 g Carb, 4 g Sugar, 1 g Fib, 30 g Prot, 28 mg Calc.

Stay On Track
You can tame the heat and add some great color to this zesty stew by topping each serving with ¼ cup peeled chopped orange and sprinkling of cilantro.

braised beef with winter vegetables

SERVES 4

- **1 pound lean beef bottom round steak, trimmed**
- **¼ teaspoon salt**
- **¼ teaspoon black pepper**
- **3 cups reduced-sodium beef broth**
- **3 fresh thyme sprigs or ½ teaspoon dried**
- **½ teaspoon five-spice powder**
- **1 bay leaf**
- **½ pound baby-cut carrots**
- **½ pound turnips, peeled and cut into 1-inch pieces**
- **½ pound small red potatoes, halved**
- **½ small head green cabbage, cut into 4 wedges**
- **¼ cup chopped fresh parsley**

1 Sprinkle beef with salt and pepper. Spray Dutch oven with nonstick spray and set over medium-high heat. Add beef and cook, turning once, until browned, about 6 minutes. Transfer beef to plate. Add ½ cup broth and bring to boil, scraping any browned bits from bottom of Dutch oven with spoon.

2 Return beef to Dutch oven. Add remaining 2 ½ cups broth, thyme, five-spice powder, and bay leaf; bring to boil. Reduce heat; cover and simmer 30 minutes. Add carrots, turnips, and potatoes; arrange cabbage on top of beef and vegetables. Cover and simmer until beef and vegetables are fork-tender, about 30 minutes.

3 Transfer beef to cutting board and let cool 10 minutes. Cut into 8 slices. Remove and discard thyme sprigs and bay leaf from vegetables and sauce in pan; stir in parsley. Serve with beef.

Per serving (2 slices beef and 2 cups vegetables and sauce): 318 Cal, 8 g Total Fat, 3 g Sat Fat, 0 g Trans Fat, 88 mg Chol, 326 mg Sod, 25 g Carb, 10 g Sugar, 6 g Fib, 36 g Prot, 96 mg Calc.

For Your Information
If you don't have five-spice powder, you can substitute ⅛ teaspoon each ground cloves, ground cinnamon, ground all-spice, and ground black pepper.

spaghetti squash with garden meatballs

SERVES 4

- ▲ **1 pound ground lean beef (7% fat or less)**
- ▲ **1 cup shredded zucchini**
- ▲ **3 ounces cremini mushrooms, finely chopped**
- ▲ **2 scallions, finely chopped**
- **1 garlic clove, crushed through press**
- **¾ teaspoon Italian seasoning blend**
- **½ teaspoon olive oil**
- ▲ **1 onion, chopped**
- **⅛ teaspoon red pepper flakes**
- ▲ **3 cups basil and garlic tomato sauce**
- ▲ **1 small (2-pound) spaghetti squash, pricked several times with fork**
- **¼ cup fresh basil leaves, thinly sliced**

1 Mix together beef, zucchini, mushrooms, scallions, garlic, and Italian seasoning in large bowl until combined. With damp hands, shape mixture into 12 meatballs.

2 Heat oil in large nonstick skillet with lid over medium heat. Add 6 meatballs and cook, turning occasionally, until browned on all sides, about 8 minutes. With slotted spoon, transfer meatballs to plate. Repeat with remaining 6 meatballs.

3 Add onion to skillet and cook, covered, stirring occasionally, until tender, about 5 minutes. Add pepper flakes and cook, stirring, just until fragrant, about 30 seconds. Stir in tomato sauce and meatballs; bring to boil. Reduce heat; cover and simmer until meatballs are cooked through, about 20 minutes, turning meatballs once halfway through cooking time.

4 Meanwhile, place squash on double layer of paper towels in microwave. Microwave on High until tender, about 8 minutes, turning once halfway through microwaving time. Let stand 5 minutes, then split squash lengthwise and scoop out and discard seeds. With fork, scrape out squash pulp and divide evenly among 4 bowls and top with meatballs and sauce. Sprinkle with basil.

Per serving (3 meatballs, ¾ cup sauce, and ¾ cup squash): 292 Cal, 7 g Total Fat, 3 g Sat Fat, 0 g Trans Fat, 69 mg Chol, 919 mg sodium, 30 g Carb, 11 g Sugar, 6 g Fib, 28 g Prot, 78 mg Calc.

SPAGHETTI
SQUASH WITH
GARDEN
MEATBALLS

roasted-garlic beef stew with burgundy

SERVES 4

2 heads garlic

2 tablespoons all-purpose flour

1 pound lean beef bottom round steak, trimmed and cut into 1-inch chunks

½ teaspoon salt

¼ teaspoon black pepper

2 onions, chopped

½ cup Burgundy or other hearty red wine

3 large carrots, thinly sliced

2 large parsnips, peeled and diced

1 ½ cups reduced-sodium beef broth

2 fresh rosemary sprigs or ½ teaspoon dried

1 cup frozen green peas

2 tablespoons chopped fresh parsley

1 Preheat oven to 400°F. Wrap garlic in foil and roast until soft and fragrant, 50–60 minutes. Let cool. Squeeze out garlic pulp and reserve.

2 Meanwhile, place flour on sheet of wax paper. Sprinkle beef with salt and pepper; coat with flour, shaking off excess. Reserve remaining flour.

3 Spray Dutch oven with nonstick spray and set over medium-high heat. Add beef; cook, stirring occasionally, until browned, about 6 minutes. Transfer beef to plate. Add onions and cook, stirring occasionally, until softened, about 5 minutes. Stir in wine; simmer until reduced by half, 4–5 minutes. Add carrots, parsnips, broth, and rosemary; bring to boil. Reduce heat; cover and simmer until vegetables are tender, about 15 minutes.

4 Return beef and any accumulated juices to Dutch oven. Stir in garlic pulp and peas. Transfer 2 tablespoons cooking liquid to small bowl; add reserved flour and whisk until smooth. Add to Dutch oven and cook, stirring, until thickened, 1–2 minutes. Stir in parsley.

Per serving (1 ½ cups): 392 Cal, 8 g Total Fat, 3 g Sat Fat, 0 g Trans Fat, 88 mg Chol, 443 mg Sod, 40 g Carb, 13 g Sugar, 8 g Fib, 36 g Prot, 123 mg Calc.

Make Ahead

This is an ideal recipe to double: Serve it one night, and then freeze the remainder for up to 3 months. A double batch will fit in a medium (4- to 6-quart) Dutch oven and cooking times should remain about the same, although we suggest you brown the beef in two batches.

classic firehouse chili
SERVES 4

2 teaspoons sunflower oil

▲ 1 pound ground lean beef (7% fat or less)

▲ 1 cup diced onion

▲ 1 small green bell pepper, seeded and chopped

2 garlic cloves, finely chopped

1 tablespoon chili powder

½ teaspoon cayenne, or to taste

½ teaspoon salt

1 tablespoon tomato paste

▲ 1 (14-ounce) can no-salt-added kidney beans, rinsed and drained

▲ 1 (14-ounce) can no-salt-added diced fire-roasted tomatoes

▲ 1 cup reduced-sodium beef broth

▲ ½ cup shredded fat-free Cheddar cheese

1 Heat oil in large saucepan over medium-high heat. Add beef; cook, stirring occasionally, until browned, about 8 minutes. Reserve ¼ cup diced onion for garnish. Add remaining ¾ cup onion, bell pepper, garlic, chili powder, cayenne, and salt. Cook, stirring frequently, until vegetables soften, about 5 minutes.

2 Stir in tomato paste; cook, stirring, 2 minutes. Add beans, tomatoes, and broth; bring to boil. Reduce heat to medium-low. Simmer, uncovered, stirring occasionally, until chili thickens, about 10 minutes.

3 Serve chili garnished with reserved diced onion and Cheddar cheese.

Per serving (1 ¼ cups chili and 2 tablespoons cheese): 331 Cal, 9 g Total Fat, 3 g Sat Fat, 0 g Trans Fat, 71 mg Chol, 552 mg Sod, 26 g Carb, 7 g Sugar, 10 g Fib, 36 g Prot, 209 mg Calc.

For Your Information
Wake up the flavors and aromas of spices by adding them to the pot at the beginning of cooking. Cooking them quickly with the onion in step 1 increases their impact in the finished chili.

THE SLOW-COOKER SOLUTION

Do your prep work when you have a few free moments, either the night before or early in the morning, then leave the rest to your slow cooker. The results? Deep, rich flavor; meltingly tender meats and poultry; perfectly cooked grains and beans; and a kitchen filled with wonderful aromas. Keep these tips in mind for optimal use of your cooker.

Fill it properly. Most slow cookers should be filled between half full and three-quarters full for best results. Consult your manufacturer's instructions for optimal use, and make any adjustments to your recipe accordingly.

Stir only as directed. Don't be tempted to open the lid during the cooking process; doing so will increase the cooking time. Stirring is not usually necessary during slow-cooking and could compromise your dish.

Thaw frozen foods first. Don't use frozen meats or poultry in a slow cooker; they may cause the dish to remain at an unsafe temperature long enough to encourage the growth of harmful bacteria.

Use nonstick spray. For easy cleanup, spray the cooker with nonstick spray before you add the ingredients.

Make ahead. You can assemble all the ingredients for a slow-cooker dish in the cooking insert the night before and store it, covered, in your refrigerator. Don't, however, place the chilled insert directly into a preheated base as sudden temperature changes can cause it to crack.

Choose a setting. If you have a choice between cooking your food on the high setting or on the low setting, as a general rule you should opt for low. Most slow cookers will heat more evenly on low, and most foods will produce higher quality results with longer, slower cooking. There are many exceptions, however, so let your recipe and your schedule be the determining factor.

Think beyond dinner. Slow-cooker recipes cooked overnight can be just the ticket for busy mornings, company brunch, or take-and-go lunches.

TRY THESE TASTY RECIPES

Cider-Braised Slow-Cooker Brisket, p 257

Creamy Slow-Cooker Grits with Eggs and Collards, p 11

Hearty Slow-Cooker Bolognese with Penne, p 101

Multigrain Slow-Cooker Porridge, p 24

Risotto-Style Slow-Cooker Barley and Peas, p 192

Slow-Cooker Apple-and-Sausage Strata, p 9

Slow-Cooker Beef and Barley Soup with Rosemary, p 39

Slow-Cooker Brunswick Stew, p 76

Slow-Cooker Caramelized Apples, p 223

Slow-Cooker Chicken Fricassee Casserole, p 168

Slow-Cooker Coq au Vin with Mushrooms and Parsnips, p 86

Slow-Cooker Georgia Garden Gumbo Soup, p 42

Slow-Cooker Sausage and Peppers over Spaghetti, p 107

Slow-Cooker Smoky BBQ Beans, p 265

Slow-Cooker Stuffed Turkey Breast with Figs and Prosciutto, p 87

Slow-Cooker Tropical Pot Roast, p 64

Tempeh, Vegetable, and Stout Slow-Cooker Chili, p 94

pork and cabbage goulash with dilled dumplings

SERVES 4

¾ pound lean boneless pork shoulder, trimmed and cut into 1-inch cubes

¼ teaspoon black pepper

▲ 1 large onion, chopped

2 garlic cloves, finely chopped

1 tablespoon paprika

▲ 3 cups reduced-sodium chicken broth

1 tablespoon tomato paste

▲ 2 cups thinly sliced Savoy cabbage

1 cup low-fat buttermilk baking mix

1 tablespoon chopped fresh dill

▲ 5 tablespoons fat-free milk

1 Preheat oven to 375°F. Sprinkle pork with pepper. Spray Dutch oven with nonstick spray and set over medium-high heat. Add half of pork and cook, turning occasionally, until browned on all sides, about 4 minutes. Transfer pork to plate. Repeat with remaining pork.

2 Spray Dutch oven again with nonstick spray and return to medium heat. Add onion and cook, covered, stirring occasionally, until tender, about 4 minutes. Add garlic and paprika; cook, stirring, until fragrant, about 30 seconds. Stir in pork, broth, and tomato paste. Bring to boil, scraping any browned bits from bottom of pan with spoon. Cover and bake 1 hour. Stir in cabbage; cover and bake 15 minutes.

3 Combine baking mix and dill in medium bowl. Stir in buttermilk just until soft dough forms. Drop dough by rounded spoonfuls onto simmering stew, making 4 dumplings. Bake, uncovered, until dumplings are golden and pork is fork-tender, about 20 minutes.

Per serving (about ¾ cup stew and 1 dumpling): 403 Cal, 10 g Total Fat, 3 g Sat Fat, 0 g Trans Fat, 56 mg Chol, 887 mg Sod, 49 g Carb, 8 g Sugar, 4 g Fib, 27 g Prot, 150 mg Calc.

Stay On Track
Steamed baby carrots sprinkled with parsley and lemon juice make a great side dish to this hearty stew.

sizzling pork with eggplant

SERVES 4

- **1 small (½-pound) eggplant, diced**
- **¼ teaspoon chili oil**
- **2 garlic cloves, finely chopped**
- **1 teaspoon grated peeled fresh ginger**
- **6 shiitake mushrooms, stems discarded, caps thinly sliced**
- **¾ pound ground lean pork**
- **½ cup reduced-sodium chicken broth**
- **2 tablespoons reduced-sodium soy sauce**
- **4 teaspoons mirin**
- **½ teaspoon black pepper**
- **8 Boston lettuce leaves**
- **2 scallions, cut into matchstick strips**

1 Put eggplant in steamer basket; set basket in large deep skillet over 1 inch of boiling water. Cover tightly and steam until eggplant is tender, about 15 minutes. Transfer eggplant to plate; drain skillet.

2 Heat oil in skillet over medium heat. Add garlic and ginger; cook, stirring frequently, just until fragrant, about 30 seconds. Add mushrooms. Increase heat to medium high and cook, stirring, 2 minutes. Add pork and cook, breaking it apart with spoon, until no longer pink, about 4 minutes. Stir in eggplant, broth, soy sauce, mirin, and pepper; bring to boil. Reduce heat and cook until flavors are blended and liquid reduces slightly, about 5 minutes.

3 Arrange 2 lettuce leaves on each of 4 plates. Top lettuce evenly with pork mixture, and serve sprinkled with scallions.

Per serving (¾ cup pork mixture with 2 lettuce leaves): 165 Cal, 5 g Total Fat, 1 g Sat Fat, 0 g Trans Fat, 50 mg Chol, 313 mg Sod, 11 g Carb, 4 g Sugar, 3 g Fib, 18 g Prot, 37 mg Calc.

Stay On Track

For a heartier dish, prepare the recipe as directed, but add 1 cup ready-cooked brown rice at the end of step 2 and cook until hot, about 2 minutes. The per-serving *PointsPlus* value will increase by *1.*

pan-grilled pork chops with smoky corn salsa

SERVES 4

1 tablespoon white wine

1 teaspoons olive oil

2 teaspoons packed brown sugar

1 teaspoon dried oregano

¾ teaspoon smoked paprika

¾ teaspoon ground cumin

▲ 4 (¼-pound) lean boneless pork loin chops, trimmed

▲ 2 ears corn on the cob

½ small avocado, pitted, peeled, and diced

▲ ¼ cup finely chopped red onion

1 tablespoon chopped fresh cilantro

Juice of ½ lime

½ teaspoon salt

¼ teaspoon black pepper

Lime wedges for serving

1 Combine wine, oil, brown sugar, oregano, paprika, and cumin in zip-close plastic bag; add pork chops. Squeeze out air and seal bag; turn to coat pork chops. Refrigerate, turning bag occasionally, at least 1 hour or overnight.

2 Spray corn lightly with nonstick spray. Set ridged grill pan over medium-high heat until very hot. Place corn in pan and grill, turning occasionally, until evenly browned, 10–12 minutes. Transfer to cutting board and let cool slightly. Cut kernels from ears of corn; transfer to medium bowl. Stir in avocado, onion, cilantro, lime juice, ¼ teaspoon salt, and ⅛ teaspoon pepper.

3 Remove pork chops from marinade; discard marinade. Sprinkle pork chops with remaining ¼ teaspoon salt and remaining ⅛ teaspoon pepper. Spray grill pan with nonstick spray and set over medium-high heat until very hot. Place pork chops in pan and grill until instant-read thermometer inserted into side of chop registers 145°F, about 4 minutes per side. Serve pork chops with salsa and lime wedges.

Per serving (1 pork chop and ½ cup salsa): 251 Cal, 11 g Total Fat, 2 g Sat Fat, 0 g Trans Fat, 66 mg Chol, 345 mg Sod, 14 g Carb, 4 g Sugar, 3 g Fib, 23 g Prot, 35 mg Calc.

For Your Information
If corn on the cob isn't in season, thaw 1 ½ cups frozen corn kernels, pat dry, and toast them in a heavy cast-iron pan over medium-high heat until they are just browned, about 6 minutes.

**PAN-GRILLED
PORK CHOPS
WITH SMOKY
CORN SALSA**

slow-cooker brunswick stew

SERVES 8

- 2 onions, diced
- 1 red bell pepper, sliced
- 3 garlic cloves, thinly sliced
- ¾ teaspoon salt
- 1 (3½-pound) chicken, cut into 10 pieces, skin and wings discarded or saved for another purpose
- 2 slices Canadian bacon, finely chopped
- 1 (14 ½-ounce) can diced tomatoes
- 1 (14-ounce) can reduced-sodium chicken broth
- 1 tablespoon Worcesteshire sauce
- 1 teaspoon hot pepper sauce
- 1 (10-ounce) package frozen cut okra, thawed
- 2 cups frozen succotash, thawed
- 1 teaspoon chopped fresh thyme

1 Combine onions, bell pepper, garlic, and salt in 5- or 6-quart slow cooker. Top with chicken and bacon. Mix tomatoes, broth, Worcestershire sauce, and pepper sauce in medium bowl; pour over chicken and bacon. Cover and cook until chicken and vegetables are fork-tender, 3–4 hours on high or 6–8 hours on low.

2 Stir okra, succotash, and thyme into slow cooker. Cover and cook on high until okra is crisp-tender, about 30 minutes.

Per serving (1 piece chicken and 1 cup vegetables and **sauce**): 248 Cal, 5 g Total Fat, 1 g Sat Fat, 0 g Trans Fat, 82 mg Chol, 565 mg Sod, 17 g Carb, 6 g Sugar, 4 g Fib, 35 g Prot, 78 mg Calc.

For Your Information

Brunswick stew, a Southern classic, was originally prepared with squirrel or rabbit. Now popular with chicken and veggies, it's excellent served with cornbread. Try it with our Scallion-Walnut Cornbread, page 206.

tandoori-style lamb chops with zucchini
SERVES 4

- ⅓ cup plain fat-free yogurt
- **1 tablespoon chopped fresh cilantro**
- **2 teaspoons curry powder**
- **2 garlic cloves, minced**
- **1 teaspoon grated peeled fresh ginger**
- **Pinch cayenne**
- **4 (5-ounce) lean bone-in lamb loin chops, trimmed**
- **2 zucchini, each cut lengthwise into 4 slices**
- **¼ teaspoon black pepper**
- **½ teaspoon salt**

1 Combine yogurt, cilantro, curry powder, garlic, ginger, and cayenne in zip-close plastic bag; add lamb chops. Squeeze out air and seal bag; turn to coat lamb chops. Refrigerate, turning bag occasionally, 8 hours or overnight.

2 Spray zucchini with nonstick spray; sprinkle with pepper and ¼ teaspoon of salt. Set ridged grill pan over medium-high heat until very hot. Place half of zucchini in pan and grill until tender, about 3 minutes per side. Transfer to platter. Repeat with remaining zucchini.

3 Meanwhile, remove lamb chops from marinade; discard marinade. Sprinkle lamb chops with remaining ¼ teaspoon salt.

4 Spray grill pan with nonstick spray and return to medium-high heat until very hot. Place lamb chops in pan and grill until instant-read thermometer inserted into side of chop registers 145°F for medium, 4–5 minutes per side. Transfer lamb chops to platter and serve with zucchini.

Per serving (1 lamb chop with 2 slices zucchini): 162 Cal, 6 g Total Fat, 2 g Sat Fat, 0 g Trans Fat, 57 mg Chol, 367 mg Sod, 6 g Carb, 3 g Sugar, 1 g Fib, 20 g Prot, 75 mg Calc.

Stay On Track
Toss 2 cups hot cooked whole wheat couscous with 2 tablespoons chopped cilantro to serve alongside these succulent lamb chops. A ½-cup portion will up the per-serving **PointsPlus** value by **3**.

SAVORY LEMON-PARSLEY MILLET p 188

THROW-IT-IN-THE-POT LAMB STEW

throw-it-in-the-pot lamb stew

SERVES 4

- 1 ½ pounds lean boneless leg of lamb, trimmed and cut into 1 ½-inch chunks
- 1 large onion, finely chopped
- 1 clove garlic, minced
- 4 teaspoons tomato paste
- 1 ½ teaspoons chopped fresh rosemary
- ½ teaspoon salt
- ¼ teaspoon black pepper
- 1 pound baby-cut carrots
- 4 celery stalks, cut into 1-inch pieces
- 2 zucchini, cut into 1 ½-inch pieces

1 Preheat oven to 325°F. Combine lamb, onion, garlic, tomato paste, rosemary, salt, and pepper in large Dutch oven. Cover and bake 1 hour.

2 Stir in carrots and celery; cover and bake 30 minutes. Stir in zucchini. Cover and bake until lamb and vegetables are fork-tender, about 20 minutes.

Per serving (2 cups): 324 Cal, 9 g Total Fat, 3 g Sat Fat, 0 g Trans Fat, 109 mg Chol, 603 mg Sod, 22 g Carb, 12 g Sugar, 6 g Fib, 38 g Prot, 88 mg Calc.

For Your Information

Unlike braised stews, where lots of liquid is added to the pot, this lamb and onion mixture is placed in a dry pot—so it's left to cook in nothing more than the essence of its own juices. The result? Intense, meaty flavor with no added fat.

chicken curry in a hurry

SERVES 4

1 tablespoon curry powder

1 tablespoon water

1 teaspoon ground cumin

1 teaspoon tomato paste

1 garlic clove, minced

½ teaspoon salt

¼ teaspoon black pepper

Pinch allspice

2 teaspoons canola oil

1 onion, diced

4 (5-ounce) skinless boneless chicken breasts

1 Fuji or Golden Delicious apple, cut into 1 ½-inch pieces

2 carrots, thinly sliced

¾ cup reduced-sodium chicken broth

1 cup frozen peas

1 Combine curry powder, water, cumin, tomato paste, garlic, salt, pepper, and allspice in small bowl; stir until smooth.

2 Heat oil in large Dutch oven over medium-high heat. Add onion and cook, stirring occasionally, until golden, 3–4 minutes. Add spice mixture and cook, stirring frequently, until fragrant, about 1 minute. Add chicken and cook until lightly browned, 1–2 minutes per side.

3 Stir in apple, carrots, and broth. Reduce heat; cover and simmer until chicken is cooked through and vegetables are tender, about 10 minutes, stirring once halfway through cooking time. Stir in peas and cook until heated through, about 2 minutes.

Per serving (1 chicken breast and ¾ cup vegetables and sauce): 256 Cal, 6 g Total Fat, 1 g Sat Fat, 0 g Trans Fat, 78 mg Chol, 431 mg Sod, 18 g Carb, 10 g Sugar, 5 g Fib, 31 g Prot, 58 mg Calc.

buffalo chicken chili

SERVES 4

2 teaspoons canola oil

△ 1 pound ground skinless chicken breast

△ 1 onion, chopped

△ 2 celery stalks, chopped

△ 2 carrots, chopped

1 (12-ounce) bottle light beer

△ 1 cup reduced-sodium chicken broth

⅓ cup hot pepper sauce, or to taste

△ 1 (14-ounce) can diced fire-roasted tomatoes

¼ cup crumbled Gorgonzola cheese

¼ cup light sour cream

1 Heat oil in large saucepan over medium heat. Add chicken; cook, stirring occasionally, until browned, about 8 minutes. Add onion, celery, and carrots; cook, stirring occasionally, until softened, about 5 minutes.

2 Add beer, broth, pepper sauce, and tomatoes; bring to boil. Simmer, stirring occasionally, until thickened, about 15 minutes.

3 Garnish each serving of chili with 1 tablespoon each Gorgonzola and sour cream.

Per serving (1 ¾ cups chili, 1 tablespoon cheese, and 1 tablespoon sour cream)**:** 293 Cal, 11 g Total Fat, 4 g Sat Fat, 0 g Trans Fat, 78 mg Chol, 989 mg Sod, 16 g Carb, 8 g Sugar, 3 g Fib, 29 g Prot, 135 mg Calc.

Stay On Track
For more flavor and fiber, add a cup of rinsed, drained black beans to the chili along with the tomatoes. The per-serving *PointsPlus* value will increase by *1.*

BUFFALO CHICKEN CHILI p 81;
SCALLION-WALNUT CORNBREAD p 206

tarragon chicken with mushrooms

SERVES 4

- ▲ 4 (4-ounce) thin-sliced chicken cutlets
- ½ teaspoon salt
- ¼ teaspoon black pepper
- ½ teaspoon olive oil
- ¼ cup (1 ounce) diced pancetta
- 2 shallots, sliced
- ▲ 1 (4-ounce) package sliced assorted mushrooms
- 1 tablespoon all-purpose flour
- ⅓ cup white wine
- ▲ ¾ cup reduced-sodium chicken broth
- ▲ ¾ cup frozen peas, thawed
- 1 tablespoon chopped fresh parsley
- 2 teaspoons chopped fresh tarragon

1 Sprinkle chicken with salt and pepper. Heat oil in large nonstick skillet over medium heat. Add chicken and cook until golden, 2–3 minutes per side. Transfer to plate.

2 Add pancetta to skillet and cook, stirring occasionally, until lightly browned, about 2 minutes. Add shallots and cook, covered, stirring occasionally, until tender, 1–2 minutes. Add mushrooms and cook until tender, about 3 minutes. Add flour and cook, stirring constantly, 1 minute.

3 Stir in wine and bring to boil. Add broth and chicken; return to boil. Reduce heat and cook, covered, until chicken is cooked through, about 3 minutes. Add peas and cook, stirring occasionally, until hot, 1–2 minutes. Remove skillet from heat; stir in parsley and tarragon.

Per serving (1 chicken cutlet and ½ cup vegetables and **sauce**): 201 Cal, 4 g Total Fat, 1 g Sat Fat, 0 g Trans Fat, 68 mg Chol, 566 mg Sod, 9 g Carb, 2 g Sugar, 1 g Fib, 27 g Prot, 29 mg Calc.

Stay On Track

Serve this flavor-packed dish with steamed red potatoes. A ⅔-cup portion sprinkled with salt and pepper will increase the per-serving *PointsPlus* value by *2*.

chicken stew with fennel and saffron
SERVES 6

6 (4-ounce) skinless chicken thighs, trimmed

¼ teaspoon salt

¼ teaspoon black pepper

1 red onion, thinly sliced

1 fennel bulb, thinly sliced

3 garlic cloves, thinly sliced

¼ teaspoon saffron threads, crushed

⅓ cup white wine

1 (14 ½-ounce) can diced tomatoes, drained

1 ¼ cups reduced-sodium chicken broth

6 baby potatoes, halved

1 ½ teaspoons fresh thyme leaves

1 Preheat oven to 350°F. Sprinkle chicken with salt and pepper. Spray large Dutch oven with nonstick spray and set over medium-high heat. Add chicken and cook until browned, about 3 minutes per side. Transfer to plate.

2 Spray Dutch oven again with nonstick spray and return to medium heat. Add onion and fennel. Cook, covered, stirring occasionally, until vegetables are tender, 6–8 minutes. Add garlic and saffron; cook, stirring frequently, until fragrant, about 30 seconds. Add wine and boil 1 minute. Stir in chicken and accumulated juices, tomatoes, broth, potatoes, and thyme; return to boil. Cover and bake until chicken and potatoes are fork-tender, about 40 minutes.

Per serving (1 chicken thigh and about 1 cup vegetables and sauce): 339 Cal, 9 g Total Fat, 3 g Sat Fat, 0 g Trans Fat, 74 mg Chol, 365 mg sodium, 36 g Carb, 5 g Sugar, 5 g Fib, 26 g Prot, 66 mg Calc.

Stay On Track
For a veggie boost, you can add 2 thickly sliced carrots to this recipe along with the potatoes in step 2.

slow-cooker coq au vin with mushrooms and parsnips

SERVES 4

- ▲ **1 (10-ounce) package cremini mushrooms, halved**
- ▲ **2 cups frozen pearl onions**
- **3 slices reduced-fat bacon, chopped**
- **4 (½-pound) skinless whole chicken legs, trimmed**
- **1 teaspoon dried thyme**
- **½ teaspoon salt**
- **¼ teaspoon black pepper**
- ▲ **1 onion, chopped**
- ▲ **2 parsnips, peeled and diced**
- **4 garlic cloves, chopped**
- **1 cup dry red wine**
- **2 tablespoons sun-dried tomato paste**
- **1 bay leaf**
- ▲ **¾ cup reduced-sodium chicken broth**

1 Combine mushrooms and pearl onions in 5- or 6-quart slow cooker. Cook bacon in large nonstick skillet over medium heat until crisp, about 4 minutes. With slotted spoon, transfer bacon to paper towels and drain. Transfer bacon to an airtight container and refrigerate.

2 Sprinkle chicken with thyme, salt, and pepper. Return skillet to medium heat. Add chicken and cook until browned, 5–6 minutes per side. Place chicken over vegetables in slow cooker.

3 Add onion and parsnips to skillet. Cook, covered, stirring occasionally, until onion is tender, 3–4 minutes. Add garlic and cook, stirring, until fragrant, about 30 seconds. Add wine, tomato paste, and bay leaf; bring to boil, stirring to blend in tomato paste. Pour wine mixture and broth over chicken. Cover and cook until chicken and vegetables are fork-tender, 3–4 hours on high or 6–8 hours on low.

4 Discard bay leaf and stir in bacon.

Per serving (1 chicken leg with about 1 cup vegetables and sauce): 328 Cal, 8 g Total Fat, 2 g Sat Fat, 0 g Trans Fat, 64 mg Chol, 527 mg Sod, 29 g Carb, 9 g Sugar, 5 g Fib, 24 g Protein, 78 mg Calc.

For Your Information

Coq au vin is traditionally prepared with a full-bodied French burgundy, but it's also delicious with lighter reds like American pinot noir. If you prefer not to use wine, substitute 1 tablespoon balsamic vinegar and an additional 1 cup broth.

slow-cooker stuffed turkey breast with figs and prosciutto

8 small dried figs, halved

1 tablespoon Marsala

1 tablespoon chopped fresh rosemary

2 large garlic cloves, finely chopped

¾ teaspoon salt

½ teaspoon black pepper

1 boneless turkey breast half (about 2 ½ pounds), skin on

4 (½-ounce) slices prosciutto

2 carrots, thickly sliced

2 celery stalks, thickly sliced

1 onion, thickly sliced

½ cup reduced-sodium chicken broth

1 Mix together figs and marsala in small bowl. Let stand, stirring occasionally, until marsala is absorbed, about 25 minutes.

2 Meanwhile, combine rosemary, garlic, salt, and pepper in cup. Remove skin from turkey breast; reserve. Place turkey, skinned side up, on cutting board. Holding sharp knife parallel to board and cutting from one long side, cut three quarters of the way through and open up breast like a book. Cover with sheet of plastic wrap. With meat mallet or rolling pin, pound to ½-inch thickness. Sprinkle with half of rosemary mixture. Layer prosciutto on turkey, leaving ½-inch border, and scatter figs evenly on top. Starting at one narrow end, roll up jelly-roll fashion. Sprinkle roll with remaining herb mixture. Cover roll with turkey skin and tie with kitchen string at 1-inch intervals.

3 Combine carrots, celery, onion, and broth in 5- or 6-quart slow cooker; top with turkey roll. Cover and cook until turkey is fork-tender, 2 ½–3 hours on high or 5–6 hours on low.

4 Transfer turkey to cutting board and keep warm. To make sauce, strain cooking liquid into glass measure; discard vegetables. Skim off fat from liquid and discard. Remove string and skin from turkey roll and cut into 16 slices. Serve with sauce.

Per serving (2 slices turkey and about 2 tablespoons sauce): 208 Cal, 2 g Total Fat, 1 g Sat Fat, 0 g Trans Fat, 99 mg Chol, 497 mg Sod, 10 g Carb, 6 g Sugar, 2 g Fib, 37 g Prot, 46 mg Calc.

stir-fry turkey with broccolini

SERVES 4

3 teaspoons canola oil

1 pound thin-sliced turkey breast cutlets, cut into strips

½ teaspoon salt

¼ teaspoon black pepper

1 red onion, sliced

1 yellow bell pepper, sliced

2 garlic cloves, finely chopped

2 (¾-pound) bunches Broccolini (Asparation), cut into 2-inch pieces

¼ cup water

2 ½ tablespoons Asian sweet chili sauce

1 tablespoon lime juice

1 Heat wok or large skillet over high heat until a drop of water sizzles on it. Pour in 1½ teaspoons oil and swirl to coat wok. Add turkey, sprinkle with salt and pepper, and stir-fry until cooked through, about 3 minutes. Transfer to plate.

2 Heat remaining 1½ teaspoons oil in wok. Add onion and bell pepper; stir-fry until crisp-tender, about 2 minutes. Add garlic and stir-fry just until fragrant, about 30 seconds. Add Broccolini and water. Cook, covered, stirring occasionally, until liquid evaporates and Broccolini is crisp-tender, 3–4 minutes.

3 Add turkey, chili sauce, and lime juice; cook until heated through, about 1 minute.

Per serving (1 ¾ cups): 244 Cal, 3 g Total Fat, 0 g Sat Fat, 0 g Trans Fat, 45 mg Chol, 534 mg Sod, 20 g Carb, 8 g Sugar, 3 g Fib, 35 g Prot, 136 mg Calc.

For Your Information
Broccolini, a cross between broccoli and Chinese broccoli, is similar to regular broccoli, but with smaller florets and long, slender stalks. If you can't find Broccolini, substitute an equal amount of asparagus.

**STIR-FRY TURKEY
WITH BROCCOLINI**

turkey, cannellini, and butternut chili
SERVES 4

- ¾ pound ground skinless turkey breast
- 1 bell pepper, chopped
- 1 onion, chopped
- 3 garlic cloves, minced
- 1 tablespoon chili powder
- 2 teaspoons ground cumin
- 1 (15 ½-ounce) can cannellini (white kidney) beans, rinsed and drained
- 1 (14-ounce) can reduced-sodium chicken broth
- 1 cup water
- 1 (20-ounce) package peeled, seeded butternut squash, cut into ½-inch pieces
- ¼ cup bulgur
- ¼ cup fat-free sour cream
- 2 tablespoons chopped fresh cilantro
- 1 ½ teaspoons minced jalapeño pepper

1 Spray large saucepan with nonstick spray and set over medium-high heat. Add turkey and cook, breaking it apart with side of spoon, until no longer pink, 4–5 minutes. Stir in bell pepper, onion, and garlic; cook until vegetables soften, about 5 minutes. Stir in chili powder and cumin; cook, stirring constantly, until fragrant, about 30 seconds. Add beans, broth, water, squash, and bulgur. Bring to boil. Reduce heat and simmer, covered, until squash and bulgur are tender, about 20 minutes.

2 Stir together sour cream, cilantro, and jalapeño in small bowl. Divide chili among 4 bowls and top each serving with 1 tablespoon sour cream mixture.

Per serving (1 ½ cups chili and 1 tablespoon sour cream mixture): 339 Cal, 3 g Total Fat, 0 g Sat Fat, 0 g Trans Fat, 35 mg Chol, 422 mg Sod, 51 g Carb, 9 g Sugar, 12 g Fib, 34 g Prot, 178 mg Calc.

8

For Your Information
Using bulgur wheat in this chili makes it thick and hearty, so a smaller amount of turkey than usual produces a robust chili. The bulgur also adds a terrific amount of fiber as well as whole-grain nutrients like B vitamins and low-fat protein.

fish tagine with cinnamon

SERVES 4

- 2 teaspoons olive oil
- 1 red onion, diced
- 2 garlic cloves, finely chopped
- ½ (3-inch) cinnamon stick
- 1 (14 ½-ounce) can fire-roasted diced tomatoes
- 1 (8-ounce) bottle clam juice
- 1 pound monkfish fillet, cut into 2 ½-inch pieces
- 1 large zucchini, quartered lengthwise and sliced
- ¼ pound green beans, trimmed and halved
- ½ teaspoon salt
- ¼ teaspoon black pepper
- 2 tablespoons chopped fresh parsley
- 1 tablespoon dried currants

1 Heat oil in large saucepan over medium-high heat. Add onion and cook, stirring occasionally, until tender, 3–4 minutes. Add garlic and cinnamon stick; cook, stirring, until fragrant, about 30 seconds. Stir in tomatoes and clam juice; bring to boil. Reduce heat and simmer 5 minutes.

2 Stir in monkfish, zucchini, green beans, salt, and pepper. Return to boil. Reduce heat; cover and simmer until monkfish is just opaque in center and vegetables are crisp-tender, 6–7 minutes. Remove and discard cinnamon stick. Sprinkle with parsley and currants.

Per serving (scant 2 cups): 173 Cal, 4 g Total Fat, 1 g Sat Fat, 0 g Trans Fat, 30 mg Chol, 675 mg Sod, 14 g Carb, 8 g Sugar, 3 g Fib, 19 g Prot, 70 mg Calc.

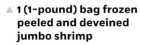

speedy shrimp, sausage, and bean stew
SERVES 4

- 1 (1-pound) bag frozen peeled and deveined jumbo shrimp
- ¼ teaspoon salt
- ¼ teaspoon black pepper
- 1 ½ teaspoons olive oil
- 1 (¼-pound) link Italian-style turkey sausage, casing removed
- 1 large shallot, thinly sliced
- 2 large plum tomatoes, diced
- 1 (15 ½-ounce) can no-salt-added navy beans, rinsed and drained
- ¾ cup reduced-sodium chicken broth
- 1 (6-ounce) bag baby spinach

1 Sprinkle shrimp with salt and pepper. Heat ½ teaspoon oil in large deep nonstick skillet over medium-high heat. Add shrimp and cook just until pink, 2–3 minutes per side. Remove from skillet and set aside.

2 Wipe out skillet. Add remaining 1 teaspoon oil and heat over medium heat. Add sausage and cook, breaking it apart with wooden spoon, until browned, about 3 minutes. Add shallot and cook, stirring occasionally, until tender, 2–3 minutes. Add tomatoes and cook, stirring occasionally, until softened, about 2 minutes. Stir in beans and broth; bring to boil. Coarsely mash mixture with potato masher or large fork.

3 Bring bean mixture back to boil; stir in shrimp and spinach. Reduce heat and cook, covered, just until spinach wilts and shrimp are opaque in center, about 2 minutes.

Per serving (about 3 shrimp and ¾ cup bean mixture):
277 Cal, 6 g Total Fat, 1 g Sat Fat, 0 g Trans Fat, 185 mg Chol, 617 mg Sod, 25 g Carb, 1 g Sugar, 8 g Fib, 31 g Prot, 140 mg Calc.

Make Ahead
Looking for an almost instant weeknight seafood meal? Prepare step 2 of this recipe, cool and refrigerate it up to 2 days in advance. When you're ready to cook the dish, sear the shrimp (no need to thaw) as directed in step 1, and then proceed to step 3.

brown rice paella with shrimp and mussels

SERVES 6

- ▲ **1 onion, chopped**
- **2 tablespoons crumbled soy chorizo**
- **3 garlic cloves, finely chopped**
- ▲ **1 cup long-grain brown rice**
- ▲ **2 cups reduced-sodium chicken broth**
- **½ teaspoon saffron threads**
- **½ teaspoon salt**
- **¼ teaspoon black pepper**
- ▲ **1 (14 ½-ounce) can diced tomatoes**
- ▲ **1 ¼ pounds large shrimp, shelled and deveined**
- ▲ **1 pound mussels, scrubbed and debearded**
- ▲ **⅔ cup frozen peas, thawed**
- **1 tablespoon chopped fresh parsley**

1 Spray Dutch oven with nonstick spray and set over medium-high heat. Add onion and chorizo. Cook, covered, stirring occasionally, until onion is tender, 3–4 minutes. Add garlic and cook, stirring frequently, until fragrant, about 30 seconds.

2 Add rice and cook, stirring, until coated, about 1 minute. Stir in broth, saffron, salt, and pepper; bring to boil. Reduce heat; cover and simmer 30 minutes. Stir in tomatoes and return to boil. Reduce heat; cover and simmer 25 minutes.

3 Stir in shrimp and mussels; return to boil. Reduce heat; cover and simmer 10 minutes. Sprinkle paella with peas, cover, and remove pot from heat. Let stand until rice is tender, shrimp are opaque in center, and mussels open, about 5 minutes. Discard any unopened mussels. Fluff rice gently with fork and sprinkle with parsley.

Per serving (¾ cup rice, 3 shrimp, and 3 or 4 mussels):
280 Cal, 4 g Total Fat, 1 g Sat Fat, 0 g Trans Fat, 153 mg Chol, 887 mg Sod, 34 g Carb, 5 g Sugar, 3 g Fib, 26 g Prot, 84 mg Calc.

For Your Information
Sometimes you'll find long hairlike strands protruding from mussels' shells. These are known as "beards," and it's usual (although not absolutely necessary) to remove them before cooking. To do so, use a paring knife to scrape off the beard.

tempeh, vegetable, and stout slow-cooker chili

- ▲ **1 onion, chopped**
- ▲ **1 turnip, peeled and chopped**
- ▲ **2 parsnips, peeled and chopped**
- ▲ **2 carrots, chopped**
- ▲ **1 small sweet potato, chopped**
- **2 teaspoons dried thyme**
- **1 (12-ounce) bottle stout beer, such as Guinness**
- ▲ **1 ½ cups reduced-sodium vegetable broth**
- **½ teaspoon salt**
- ▲ **1 (14-ounce) can no-salt-added chickpeas, drained and rinsed**
- **1 (8-ounce) package tempeh, cut into bite-size pieces**
- **¼ cup chopped fresh parsley**
- **Zest of 1 lemon**
- **6 tablespoons light sour cream**

1 In 5- or 6-quart slow cooker, combine onion, turnip, parsnips, carrots, sweet potato, thyme, beer, broth, and salt. Cover and cook until vegetables are very tender, 4–5 hours on high or 8–10 hours on low.

2 Transfer 1 cup chili to blender or food processor. Add chickpeas and puree. Stir mixture back into chili. Add tempeh and cook on high until heated through, 5–10 minutes.

3 Garnish each serving of chili with parsley, lemon zest, and 1 tablespoon sour cream.

Per serving (1 generous cup chili and 1 tablespoon sour cream): 266 Cal, 7 g Total Fat, 2 g Sat Fat, 0 g Trans Fat, 52 mg Chol, 303 mg Sod, 36 g Carb, 8 g Sugar, 7 g Fib, 13 g Prot, 150 mg Calc.

For Your Information
The chickpeas in this recipe are pureed and added to the chili at the end of cooking to thicken it. However, if you like a chili with a thinner consistency, you can skip this step and simply stir the whole chickpeas in with the tempeh.

fragrant butternut stew with apples and kale

SERVES 8

4 teaspoons olive oil

▲ 2 red onions, diced

3 garlic cloves, finely chopped

2 teaspoons ground coriander

2 teaspoons ground cumin

¾ teaspoon salt

¼ teaspoon black pepper

⅛ teaspoon cayenne

▲ 1 (2-pound) butternut squash, peeled and cut into 1-inch pieces

▲ 1 ½ pounds rutabaga or turnips, peeled and cut into 1-inch pieces

▲ 1 pound carrots, sliced

▲ 2 Granny Smith apples, peeled, cored, and cut into 1-inch pieces

▲ 1 (15-ounce) can no-salt-added kidney beans, rinsed and drained

▲ 1 (14-ounce) can reduced-sodium vegetable broth

▲ 4 cups sliced kale leaves

1 Preheat oven to 400°F. Heat oil in large Dutch oven over medium-high heat. Add onions and cook, stirring frequently, until golden, 5–6 minutes. Add garlic, coriander, cumin, salt, pepper, and cayenne. Cook, stirring frequently, just until fragrant, about 1 minute.

2 Stir in squash, rutabaga, carrots, apples, beans, and broth. Cover and bake until vegetables are tender, about 45 minutes.

3 Stir in kale. Cover and bake until kale is tender, about 10 minutes.

Per serving (generous 1 ¾ cups): 198 Cal, 3 g Total Fat, 0 g Sat Fat, 0 g Trans Fat, 0 mg Chol, 355 mg Sod, 40 g Carb, 14 g Sugar, 12 g Fib, 7 g Prot, 163 mg Calc.

Make Ahead

This veggie-rich stew is great to have on hand for quick meals. For freezing, consider dividing the stew into individual servings first, then marking each one with the per-serving *PointsPlus* value for easy tracking.

Chapter 4

perfect pastas & pizzas

perfect pastas & pizzas

spaghetti with mozzarella-stuffed meatballs

SERVES 4

- ▲ **½ pound ground lean beef (7% fat or less)**
- **¼ cup plain dried whole wheat bread crumbs**
- ▲ **¼ cup fat-free milk**
- ▲ **1 large egg white**
- **1 garlic clove, minced**
- **¼ teaspoon black pepper**
- **¼ cup + 2 tablespoons grated Parmesan cheese**
- **¼ cup + 2 tablespoons chopped fresh parsley**
- **16 (½-inch) cubes part-skim mozzarella cheese (1 ½ ounces)**
- **2 cups reduced-sodium marinara sauce**
- **½ cup water**
- ▲ **6 ounces whole wheat spaghetti**

1 Stir together beef, bread crumbs, milk, egg white, garlic, pepper, ¼ cup Parmesan, and ¼ cup parsley in large bowl. Shape beef mixture around mozzarella cubes to form 16 meatballs.

2 Bring marinara sauce and water to simmer in large skillet. Add meatballs. Cover and simmer, stirring gently a few times, until meatballs are cooked through, about 10 minutes.

3 Meanwhile, cook pasta according to package directions, omitting salt. Drain.

4 Divide pasta among 4 plates. Top each portion evenly with meatballs and sauce, and sprinkle with remaining 2 tablespoons Parmesan and 2 tablespoons parsley.

Per serving (¾ cup pasta, 4 meatballs, ⅔ cup sauce, and ½ tablespoon Parmesan): 369 Cal, 10 g Total Fat, 4 g Sat Fat, 0 g Trans Fat, 99 mg Chol, 372 mg Sod, 45 g Carb, 8 g Sugar, 7 g Fib, 26 g Prot, 224 mg Calc.

For Your Information

Be sure to cook the meatballs at a low simmer without allowing the sauce to boil vigorously; this will help to maintain their shape and prevent the mozzarella from oozing out.

HEARTY SLOW-COOKER BOLOGNESE WITH PENNE

hearty slow-cooker bolognese with penne

SERVES 8

- ▲ **1 ½ pounds ground lean beef (7% or less fat)**
- ▲ **2 (28-ounce) cans crushed tomatoes**
- ▲ **¾ cup fat-free milk**
- ▲ **2 large carrots, grated**
- ▲ **1 large Vidalia onion, grated**
- ▲ **1 small fennel bulb, trimmed and diced**
- ▲ **1 (10-ounce) package cremini mushrooms, trimmed and chopped**
- **4 garlic cloves, chopped**
- **1 tablespoon chopped fresh oregano or 1 teaspoon dried**
- **1 teaspoon salt**
- **½ teaspoon ground nutmeg**
- **1 tablespoon red-wine vinegar**
- **¾ pound penne pasta**

1 Spray 5- or 6-quart slow cooker with nonstick spray. Add beef, tomatoes, milk, carrots, onion, fennel, mushrooms, garlic, oregano, salt, and nutmeg to slow cooker. Stir to combine. Cover and cook 3–3 ½ hours on high or 6–7 hours on low.

2 Remove lid and stir in vinegar. Cook on high, uncovered, until sauce thickens slightly, about 30 minutes.

3 Cook pasta according to package directions, omitting salt. Serve pasta with sauce.

Per serving (¾ cup pasta and ¾ cup sauce): 382 Cal, 6 g Total Fat, 2 g Sat Fat, 0 g Trans Fat, 52 mg Chol, 645 mg Sod, 57 g Carb, 6 g Sugar, 8 g Fiber, 29 g Prot, 149 mg Calc.

Make Ahead

This richly flavored meat sauce is perfect for cooking and freezing for weeknight meals. Quickly cool the sauce (placing it in smaller containers and setting the containers on a wire rack is a good way to do this), and freeze as soon as it is no longer warm. Don't try to freeze cooked pasta, however—it will become mushy.

rigatoni with pancetta and goat cheese

SERVES 4

- **2 ounces thinly sliced pancetta**
- ▲ **6 ounces whole wheat rigatoni**
- **2 teaspoons olive oil**
- **3 garlic cloves, minced**
- **2 ounces goat cheese, crumbled**
- **Juice and zest of 1 lemon**
- **¼ teaspoon black pepper**
- **⅓ cup chopped fresh parsley**

1 Preheat oven to 400°F. Place pancetta on a small baking sheet and cook until browned and crisped, 15–20 minutes. Transfer to paper towels to drain. Cool and crumble.

2 Cook pasta according to package directions, omitting salt. Drain pasta, reserving ¼ cup of cooking water.

3 Meanwhile, heat oil in large nonstick skillet over medium-low heat. Add garlic and cook, stirring, until golden, about 2 minutes. Add reserved pasta cooking water, goat cheese, lemon zest and juice, and pepper; whisk until smooth. Add pasta and parsley; toss to coat. Sprinkle each serving with 1 tablespoon crumbled pancetta.

Per serving (1 cup pasta and 1 tablespoon pancetta):
258 Cal, 8 g Total Fat, 3 g Sat Fat, 0 g Trans Fat, 18 mg Chol, 443 mg Sod, 35 g Carb, 2 g Sugar, 4 g Fib, 12 g Prot, 52 mg Calc.

Stay On Track
Make this a complete meal by adding 3 cups small broccoli florets to the pasta during the last 2 minutes of cooking time. Drain and toss as directed.

creamy orecchiette with chicken and artichokes

SERVES 4

2 teaspoons olive oil

1 large shallot, minced

1 tablespoon all-purpose flour

1 (14 ½-ounce) can reduced-sodium chicken broth

2 teaspoons Dijon mustard

1 (14-ounce) can artichoke hearts in water, drained and quartered

½ cup fat-free half-and-half

Zest of 1 lemon

2 teaspoons finely chopped fresh tarragon or ½ teaspoon dried

2 garlic cloves, finely chopped

⅛ teaspoon salt

¼ teaspoon black pepper

¾ pound chicken breast tenders, trimmed and halved

6 ounces whole wheat orecchiette

1 Heat oil in large skillet over medium-high heat. Add shallot and cook, stirring frequently, until softened, 2–3 minutes. Add flour and cook, stirring constantly, until golden brown, about 1 minute. Gradually stir in broth, then mustard; bring to boil. Cook until slightly thickened, about 3 minutes. Add artichokes; reduce heat and simmer 2 minutes. Add half-and-half and cook until heated through. Cover and keep warm.

2 Meanwhile, combine lemon zest, tarragon, garlic, salt, and pepper in shallow bowl. Spray chicken tenders with nonstick olive oil spray. Add to tarragon mixture in bowl and toss to coat evenly. Spray large ridged grill pan with nonstick spray and set over medium-high heat until very hot. Cook chicken, turning occasionally, until cooked through, 5–6 minutes.

3 Cook pasta according to package directions, omitting salt. Drain pasta; transfer to skillet with artichokes and sauce. Add chicken and toss over medium-low heat until coated and heated through.

Per serving (1 generous cup pasta and sauce and 3 pieces chicken): 380 Cal, 6 g Total Fat, 1 g Sat Fat, 0 g Trans Fat, 47 mg Chol, 841 mg Sod, 51 g Carb, 4 g Sugar, 8 g Fib, 30 g Prot, 80 mg Calc.

For Your Information
A pasta shape associated with Italy's southern Puglia region, orecchiette means "little ears" in Italian, a reference to its convex, disklike shape. You can substitute medium shells or rotelle, if you like.

garlicky fettuccine with chicken and escarole

SERVES 4

- ▲ **6 ounces whole wheat fettuccine**
- ▲ **6 cups sliced escarole**
- **1 teaspoon olive oil**
- ▲ **1 large onion, chopped**
- **6 garlic cloves, sliced**
- ▲ **2 cups (8 ounces) shredded boneless skinless roast chicken breast**
- ▲ **2 plum tomatoes, chopped**
- **¾ cup dry white wine**
- **2 tablespoons chopped fresh parsley**
- **½ teaspoon salt**
- **⅛ teaspoon red pepper flakes**

1 Cook pasta according to package directions, omitting salt. Add escarole during last 5 minutes of cooking. Drain and keep warm.

2 Meanwhile, heat oil in large nonstick skillet over medium heat. Add onion and garlic, and cook, stirring occasionally, until softened, about 5 minutes. Add chicken, tomatoes, and wine. Cover and cook just until heated through, stirring frequently, about 4 minutes. Add pasta with escarole, parsley, salt, and pepper flakes; cook, tossing, until well combined. Divide among 4 plates.

Per serving (1 ¼ cups): 329 Cal, 4 g Total Fat, 1 g Sat Fat, 0 g Trans Fat, 48 mg Chol, 821 mg Sod, 42 g Carb, 4 g Sugar, 9 g Fib, 26 g Prot, 87 mg Calc.

GARLICKY FETTUCCINE WITH CHICKEN AND ESCAROLE

asian turkey noodle bowls

SERVES 6

- ¼ **pound brown rice spaghetti**
- **Grated zest and juice of 2 limes**
- **1 tablespoon packed brown sugar**
- **2 teaspoons Asian fish sauce**
- **1 ½ teaspoons chili-garlic paste**
- **2 teaspoons peanut oil**
- **1 pound ground skinless turkey breast**
- **½ teaspoon five-spice powder**
- **¼ teaspoon salt**
- **½ pound asparagus, trimmed and cut into 3-inch pieces**
- **3 garlic cloves, minced**
- **1 tablespoon minced peeled fresh ginger**
- **¼ cup chopped fresh cilantro**
- **4 tablespoons dry-roasted peanuts, coarsely chopped**

1 Cook spaghetti according to package directions, omitting salt. Rinse under cold running water; drain again and transfer to medium bowl.

2 Meanwhile, whisk together lime zest and juice, brown sugar, fish sauce, and chili-garlic paste in small bowl until sugar dissolves.

3 Heat 1 teaspoon oil in large nonstick skillet over medium-high heat. Add turkey, five-spice powder, and salt. Cook, breaking apart turkey with wooden spoon, until no longer pink and most of liquid has evaporated, about 5 minutes. Add turkey mixture to spaghetti.

4 Heat remaining 1 teaspoon oil in same skillet over medium-high heat. Add asparagus, garlic, and ginger. Cook, stirring constantly, just until asparagus turns bright green, 1–2 minutes. Add spaghetti and turkey to asparagus in skillet and cook, tossing, until heated through. Remove from heat and stir in lime mixture. Divide noodle mixture among 4 bowls; sprinkle each evenly with cilantro and peanuts. Serve at once.

Per serving (1 cup pasta and asparagus and 1 tablespoon peanuts): 224 Cal, 6 g Total Fat, 1 g Sat Fat, 0 g Trans Fat, 30 mg Chol, 324 mg Sod, 22 g Carb, 4 g Sugar, 2 g Fib, 23 g Prot, 27 mg Calc.

Make Ahead

This pasta will keep refrigerated up to 2 days. You don't even have to reheat it—enjoy it chilled, the way noodles are often served in Asian countries.

slow-cooker sausage and peppers over spaghetti

SERVES 8

- 1 (28-ounce) can crushed tomatoes
- 2 red bell peppers, seeded and cut into ½-inch strips
- 1 yellow bell pepper, seeded and cut into ½-inch strips
- 1 large red onion, cut into ½-inch slices
- 4 garlic cloves, chopped
- 1 teaspoon chopped fresh oregano or ½ teaspoon dried
- ¾ pound (3 links) sweet Italian-style turkey sausages, cut into 2-inch pieces
- ¾ pound (3 links) hot Italian-style turkey sausages, cut into 2-inch pieces
- ½ pound whole wheat spaghetti
- 2 teaspoons balsamic vinegar

1 Spray a 5- or 6-quart slow cooker with nonstick spray. Add tomatoes, bell peppers, onion, garlic, and oregano. Stir to combine. Nestle sausage pieces among vegetables. Cover and cook until vegetables are very tender and sausage is cooked through, 3 ½–4 hours on high or 7–8 hours on low.

2 Cook spaghetti according to package directions, omitting salt. Stir vinegar into sausage and peppers, and serve over spaghetti.

Per serving (1 cup sausage and peppers and ½ cup spaghetti): 299 Cal, 10 g Total Fat, 0 g Sat Fat, 0 g Trans Fat, 51 mg Chol, 683 mg Sod, 35 g Carb, 5 g Sugar, 7 g Fib, 21 g Prot, 58 mg Calc.

Stay On Track

Make a quick and refreshing salad of romaine, escarole, cucumber, and red onion tossed with red-wine vinegar, salt, and black pepper to serve alongside this hearty pasta.

MONEY-SAVING TIPS

Yes, you can prepare interesting, healthful meals without spending a fortune. Our strategies can even save you time as well as money.

Shop from a list. Not only do impulse purchases run up your grocery bill, but they're also more likely to be the types of foods you'd rather avoid. Make a list before you leave for the store and commit to sticking to it.

Check sales online. Sign up for your favorite grocery stores' sales alerts; you can have them sent straight to your smart phone. This way, you can peruse the weekly specials (especially produce in season), then plan your menus and select recipes accordingly.

Look for bulk bins. Grains, beans, nuts, and dried fruits are often available in the bulk bin aisle of supermarkets and are generally less expensive than their packaged counterparts. Additionally, you can bag up just what you need, so you don't have to pay for more than you'll use. It's a great way to experiment with new foods.

Buy warehouse quantities carefully. The big quantities sold at discount clubs only make sense if you can use the food before its expiration date. Consider splitting perishable items with a friend.

Think about what you have on hand. Using what's already in your pantry and your fridge is a top strategy for saving money. You can even use technology to help you: Enter two or more ingredients you'd like to use into a recipe search tool, like the one at weightwatchers.com, and you'll get numerous recipe suggestions.

Make use of your freezer. A closer relationship with your freezer can really pay off: Not only will it allow you to take advantage of sales on perishables like meat and poultry, but also knowing how to freeze foods before they go bad adds up to big savings.

BANG-FOR-YOUR BUCK RECIPES

While prices vary from region to region and season to season, the following main-course recipes should feed four people for a total of about $12 or less.

lemon-thyme salmon fillets over orzo

SERVES 4

- ▲ **1 cup whole wheat orzo pasta**
- **Juice of 1 lemon**
- **2 teaspoons olive oil**
- **1 tablespoon water**
- **2 teaspoons Dijon mustard**
- **2 teaspoons capers, rinsed**
- **¼ teaspoon black pepper**
- ▲ **1 pint grape tomatoes**
- **1 shallot, minced**
- **1 tablespoon chopped fresh thyme or 1 teaspoon dried**
- **½ teaspoon salt**
- ▲ **4 (¼-pound) pieces skinless wild salmon fillet**

1 Preheat oven to 425°F. Line a rimmed baking sheet with parchment paper.

2 Cook orzo according to package directions, omitting salt. Drain and place in medium bowl. In blender or mini-food processor, combine lemon juice, oil, water, mustard, capers, and pepper; pulse until capers are pureed. Pour dressing over orzo and toss to coat.

3 Meanwhile, place tomatoes, shallot, and thyme on prepared baking sheet; sprinkle with ¼ teaspoon salt. Spray with nonstick spray and toss to combine. Roast in oven 6 minutes. Push tomatoes to one side of baking sheet. Sprinkle salmon with remaining ¼ teaspoon salt and place on other side of sheet. Roast until salmon fillets are just opaque in center and tomatoes are tender, 10–12 minutes. Serve with orzo.

Per serving (½ cup orzo, 1 piece salmon, and ¼ cup tomatoes): 377 Cal, 12 g Total Fat, 2 g Sat Fat, 0 g Trans Fat, 72 mg Chol, 454 mg Sod, 35 g Carb, 2 g Sugar, 6 g Fib, 34 g Prot, 29 mg Calc.

linguine and spinach with white clam sauce

SERVES 4

- ½ pound whole wheat linguine
- 2 teaspoons olive oil
- 1 shallot, finely chopped
- 4 garlic cloves
- ½ cup white wine
- 2 (6-ounce) cans chopped clams
- 1 (6-ounce) bag baby spinach
- ¼ cup finely chopped fresh parsley
- ½ teaspoon finely grated lemon zest
- 1 teaspoon unsalted butter
- ¼ teaspoon red pepper flakes

1 Cook pasta according to package directions, omitting salt. Drain pasta, reserving ½ cup cooking water.

2 Meanwhile, heat oil in large skillet over medium-high heat. Add shallot and cook, stirring frequently, until softened, about 2 minutes. Add garlic and cook 1 minute. Stir in wine and cook until reduced by half, about 1 minute. Reduce heat to medium and add clams with juices and spinach. Cook, stirring frequently, until spinach wilts, about 2 minutes.

3 Combine pasta, clam sauce, reserved pasta cooking water, parsley, lemon zest, butter, and pepper flakes in large bowl.

Per serving (1 ½ cups pasta with sauce): 305 Cal, 7 g Total Fat, 1 g Sat Fat, 0 g Trans Fat, 10 mg Chol, 365 mg Sod, 44 g Carb, 3 g Sugar, 10 g Fib, 14 g Prot, 74 mg Calc.

Stay On Track

If you like, add 2 cups sliced yellow squash to the pasta water during the last 3 minutes of cooking. Drain and toss as directed.

fusilli primavera with shrimp

SERVES 4

- ▲ **4 plum tomatoes, halved**
- ▲ **1 large yellow bell pepper, seeded and cut into ½-inch-thick slices**
- ▲ **1 red onion, halved and cut into ½-inch-thick slices**
- **3 garlic cloves, sliced**
- **1 tablespoon olive oil**
- **½ teaspoon salt**
- **¼ teaspoon black pepper**
- ▲ **½ pound asparagus spears, trimmed and cut into 2-inch pieces**
- **6 ounces spinach fusilli**
- ▲ **¾ pound peeled cooked medium shrimp**
- **¼ cup crumbled ricotta salata cheese**
- **¼ cup sliced fresh basil leaves**

1 Preheat oven to 450°F.

2 Spray large baking pan with nonstick spray. Place tomatoes, bell pepper, onion, and garlic on pan. Drizzle with oil, sprinkle with salt and black pepper, and toss to combine. Spread vegetables in single layer and roast 15 minutes. Add asparagus to pan and toss. Continue to roast until vegetables are lightly browned and tender, about 10 minutes longer.

3 Meanwhile, cook pasta according to package directions, omitting salt. Add shrimp to pasta during last 1 minute of cooking. Drain. Combine roasted vegetables and pasta with shrimp in large bowl. Top with ricotta salata and basil.

Per serving (1 ¾ cups pasta with shrimp and vegetables with 1 tablespoon cheese): 344 Cal, 9 g Total Fat, 3 g Sat Fat, 0 g Trans Fat, 126 mg Chol, 690 mg Sod, 43 g Carb, 7 g Sugar, 7 g Fib, 24 g Prot, 101 mg Calc.

For Your Information
Ricotta salata is a traditional Sicilian cheese made from pressed, dried ricotta. If you like, substitute crumbled goat cheese for no change in **PointsPlus** value.

FUSILLI PRIMAVERA
WITH SHRIMP

tuscan kale and white bean pasta
SERVES 4

Ingredients

- **6 ounces whole wheat fusilli pasta**
- **2 teaspoons olive oil**
- **1 Vidalia or other sweet onion, halved and thinly sliced**
- **2 garlic cloves, minced**
- **1 tablespoon chopped fresh rosemary or 1 teaspoon dried**
- **1 (¾-pound) bunch Tuscan kale, stems removed and coarsely chopped, leaves sliced**
- **⅛ teaspoon salt**
- **¼ teaspoon black pepper**
- **1 (14-ounce) can petite-diced tomatoes**
- **½ cup reduced-sodium chicken broth**
- **¼ cup sun-dried tomatoes (not packed in oil), thinly sliced**
- **1 (19-ounce) can cannellini (white kidney) beans, rinsed and drained**

Directions

1 Cook pasta according to package directions, omitting salt. Drain pasta, reserving ½ cup cooking water.

2 Meanwhile, heat oil in large skillet over medium-high heat. Add onion and cook, stirring frequently, until softened, 4–5 minutes. Add garlic and rosemary; cook 1 minute. Stir in kale, salt, and pepper. Reduce heat to medium-low. Add diced tomatoes, broth, and sun-dried tomatoes. Cover skillet and cook until kale is tender, 6–7 minutes.

3 Stir in beans and cook until just heated through. Add pasta and reserved cooking water to skillet; cook, tossing, until heated through.

Per serving (1 ½ cups pasta): 402 Cal, 4 g Total Fat, 1 g Sat Fat, 0 g Trans Fat, 0 mg Chol, 777 mg Sod, 75 g Carb, 12 g Sugar, 14 g Fib, 19 g Prot, 234 mg Calc.

For Your Information

Kale has become the go-to green for many health-conscious cooks: The dark, slender-leafed variety known as Tuscan, Lacinato, or dinosaur kale has a particularly earthy flavor and tender texture, but you can substitute curly kale in this recipe as well.

smoked gouda macaroni with caramelized onion

SERVES 6

- **1 large onion, halved lengthwise and thinly sliced crosswise**
- **¼ teaspoon salt**
- **½ pound (2 cups) whole wheat elbow macaroni**
- **1 (15-ounce) can evaporated fat-free milk**
- **1 large egg**
- **1 teaspoon mustard powder**
- **1 teaspoon water**
- **1 ½ cups shredded smoked Gouda cheese**
- **1 cup fat-free cottage cheese**
- **Pinch cayenne**
- **1 tablespoon chopped fresh parsley**

1 Preheat oven to 450°F. Spray 7 x 11-inch baking dish with nonstick spray.

2 Place onion on small rimmed baking sheet; sprinkle with salt and lightly spray with nonstick spray. Spread onion over pan and bake until tender and lightly browned, about 20 minutes, stirring once halfway through cooking.

3 Meanwhile, cook pasta according to package directions, omitting salt. Drain and return to pan.

4 Place evaporated milk in small saucepan over low heat and cook until warmed, about 2 minutes. Remove from heat and whisk in egg. Stir together mustard powder and water in small cup until mustard is dissolved; whisk into milk mixture.

5 Add milk mixture, Gouda cheese, cottage cheese, and cayenne to macaroni. Cook over low heat, stirring constantly, just until mixture thickens, about 5 minutes. Transfer mixture to prepared baking dish and sprinkle with onion. Bake just until heated through, about 10 minutes. Sprinkle with parsley.

Per serving (1 cup): 335 Cal, 9 g Total Fat, 5 g Sat Fat, 0 g Trans Fat, 73 mg Chol, 569 mg Sod, 41 g Carb, 12 g Sugar, 3 g Fib, 24 g Prot, 451 mg Calc.

easy garden vegetable lasagna

SERVES 8

- 2 medium zucchini, thinly sliced lengthwise
- 1 medium yellow squash, thinly sliced lengthwise
- 1 small eggplant, thinly sliced
- 1 tablespoon olive oil
- 2 garlic cloves, minced
- ¼ teaspoon salt
- ¼ teaspoon black pepper
- 4 ½ cups low-sodium marinara sauce
- 1 (9-ounce) box no-boil lasagna noodles (16 noodles)
- 1 (15-ounce) container fat-free ricotta cheese
- ¼ cup chopped fresh basil
- 1 cup shredded reduced-fat low-sodium mozzarella cheese

1 Preheat oven to 375°F. Spray 9 x 13-inch baking dish with nonstick spray.

2 Combine zucchini, yellow squash, eggplant, oil, garlic, salt, and pepper in large microwavable bowl. Cover with plastic wrap and vent wrap on one corner. Microwave on High until vegetables soften, 4–5 minutes, stirring once about halfway through cooking time. Let cool 5 minutes and drain.

3 Spread 1 cup marinara sauce over bottom of baking dish. Cover with 5 lasagna noodles, overlapping as needed. Layer with half of vegetable mixture, dot with half of ricotta, and spread with 1 cup marinara sauce. Top with 5 noodles; then layer remaining vegetables, basil, remaining ricotta, 1 cup marinara sauce, and remaining 6 noodles. Spread remaining 1 ½ cups marinara sauce on top and sprinkle with mozzarella.

4 Spray sheet of foil with nonstick spray; cover dish with foil, sprayed side down. Bake lasagna 30 minutes. Remove foil and continue baking until mozzarella has browned slightly and noodles are very tender, about 15 minutes longer. Cool 15 minutes; then cut into 8 squares.

Per serving (1 square): 310 Cal, 6 g Total Fat, 2 g Sat Fat, 0 g Trans Fat, 12 mg Chol, 261 mg Sod, 46 g Carb, 12 g Sugar, 6 g Fib, 18 g Prot, 314 mg Calc.

Make Ahead

You can prepare the lasagna through step 3 and freeze it. We recommend using a heavy-duty foil pan available at most supermarkets. First wrap the top securely with foil; then wrap the entire pan in plastic freezer wrap.

**EASY GARDEN
VEGETABLE LASAGNA**

spaghetti with mushrooms, asparagus, and dill

SERVES 4

- ▲ **6 ounces whole wheat spaghetti**
- ▲ **1 bunch asparagus, trimmed and cut into 1½-inch pieces**
- **2 teaspoons olive oil**
- **4 shallots, thinly sliced**
- **2 garlic cloves, minced**
- ▲ **¾ pound mixed wild mushrooms**
- **½ teaspoon salt**
- **2 teaspoons all-purpose flour**
- ▲ **1 cup reduced-sodium chicken or vegetable broth**
- ▲ **¼ cup fat-free half-and-half**
- **3 tablespoons chopped fresh dill**
- **4 tablespoons grated reduced-fat Parmesan cheese**

1 Cook pasta according to package directions, omitting salt. Add asparagus during last 3 minutes of cooking. Drain.

2 Meanwhile, heat oil in large skillet over medium-high heat. Add shallots and garlic, and cook, stirring often, until shallots soften, 2–3 minutes. Add mushrooms and salt; cook, stirring occasionally, until mushrooms are tender, about 6 minutes.

3 Add flour to skillet and cook, stirring constantly, 1 minute. Gradually stir in broth; bring to boil. Reduce heat and simmer, stirring often, until liquid thickens slightly, about 3 minutes. Add half-and-half and cook until heated through. Add pasta with asparagus, dill, and 2 tablespoons Parmesan; toss to coat.

4 Divide pasta among 4 shallow bowls; sprinkle evenly with remaining 2 tablespoons Parmesan.

Per serving (1¼ cups pasta and 1 tablespoon Parmesan): 262 Cal, 4 g Total Fat, 1 g Sat Fat, 0 g Trans Fat, 4 mg Chol, 409 mg Sodium, 46 g Carb, 7 g Sugar, 8 g Fib, 15 g Prot, 140 mg Calc.

penne alla vodka with broccoli rabe
SERVES 4

- ▲ **1 bunch broccoli rabe, trimmed and cut into 3-inch pieces**
- ▲ **6 ounces whole wheat penne**
- **¼ cup vodka**
- **2 garlic cloves, minced**
- **1 ½ cups low-sodium marinara sauce**
- ▲ **⅓ cup fat-free half-and-half**
- **2 teaspoons olive oil**
- **½ teaspoon red pepper flakes**
- **¼ teaspoon salt**

1 Bring large pot of water to boil over medium-high heat. Add broccoli rabe and cook 30 seconds. Using tongs, transfer broccoli rabe to colander and drain. Add pasta to water and cook until tender, about 12 minutes.

2 Meanwhile, bring vodka and garlic to simmer in a large saucepan over medium-high heat. Simmer until vodka is reduced by half, about 1 minute. Stir in marinara sauce and half-and-half. Reduce heat to medium-low and bring sauce to simmer. Add pasta to sauce and toss to combine.

3 Heat oil in large skillet over medium-high heat. Add pepper flakes and cook, stirring, 30 seconds. Add broccoli rabe and cook, stirring occasionally, until heated through, about 5 minutes. Sprinkle with salt. Serve over or alongside pasta.

Per serving (¾ cup pasta and sauce and ¾ cup broccoli rabe): 270 Cal, 4 g Total Fat, 0 g Sat Fat, 0 g Trans Fat, 0 mg Chol, 258 mg Sod, 42 g Carb, 7 g Sugar, 5 g Fib, 8 g Prot, 80 mg Calc.

Stay On Track
For more fiber and protein, add 1 cup white beans with the marinara sauce in step 2; the per-serving **Points Plus** value will increase by **2**.

MAC-AND-CHEESE
MUFFINS

mac-and-cheese muffins
SERVES 6

- ¼ **pound (1 cup) whole wheat elbow macaroni**
- ¾ **cup fat-free half-and-half**
- 1 **tablespoon all-purpose flour**
- ¼ **teaspoon smoked paprika**
- ¼ **teaspoon salt**
- 1 **cup shredded reduced-fat Cheddar cheese**
- ¼ **cup fat-free sour cream**
- 3 **tablespoons plain dried whole wheat bread crumbs**
- 1 **teaspoon olive oil**

1 Preheat oven to 375°F. Spray 6 nonstick muffin cups with nonstick spray or line with paper liners.

2 Cook pasta in boiling water for 5 minutes only and drain. (It will continue to cook during baking.)

3 Whisk together half-and-half, flour, paprika, and salt in large saucepan. Place over medium-high heat and cook, stirring constantly, until sauce simmers and thickens, about 3 minutes. Remove from heat and stir in ¾ cup Cheddar and sour cream. Add macaroni and mix to combine. Divide macaroni mixture among muffin cups.

4 Sprinkle remaining ¼ cup cheese over muffins. Combine bread crumbs and oil in small bowl; sprinkle over muffins. Bake until bubbling and lightly brown on top, about 15 minutes. Cool in pan 10 minutes. Loosen from pans and transfer to plates.

Per serving (1 muffin): 182 Cal, 5 g Total Fat, 3 g Sat Fat, 0 g Trans Fat, 14 mg Chol, 364 mg Sod, 24 g Carb, 3 g Sugar, 2 g Fib, 10 g Prot, 345 mg Calc.

Make Ahead
Place the muffins in zip-close bags and refrigerate up to 4 days, or freeze up to 3 months. To reheat one frozen muffin, unwrap and heat in the microwave 2 minutes or in a 300°F oven until hot, about 25 minutes.

greek pasta salad

½ pound bucatini pasta

Juice of 1 lemon

1 tablespoon chopped fresh oregano or 1 teaspoon dried

1 garlic clove, finely chopped

2 teaspoons olive oil

¼ teaspoon salt

¼ teaspoon black pepper

▲ 3 plum tomatoes, diced

▲ 1 small red onion, halved lengthwise and thinly sliced

▲ ½ English (seedless) cucumber, quartered lengthwise and sliced

¼ cup pitted brine-cured black or green olives, halved

▲ ⅓ cup fat-free feta cheese, crumbled

1 Prepare pasta according to package directions, omitting salt. Rinse under cold water and drain.

2 Meanwhile, whisk together lemon juice, oregano, garlic, oil, salt, and pepper in large bowl. Add tomatoes, onion, cucumber, and olives; toss to coat.

3 Add pasta to bowl and toss again. Sprinkle with feta cheese.

Per serving (2 cups pasta salad and 1 rounded tablespoon feta): 286 Cal, 5 g Total Fat, 0 g Sat Fat, 0 g Trans Fat, 2 mg Chol, 382 mg Sod, 49 g Carb, 5 g Sugar, 6 g Fib, 12 g Prot, 105 mg Calc.

Make Ahead

This quick and easy salad is terrific to pack up for on-the-go lunches. You might want to consider doubling the recipe so your family has leftovers to enjoy throughout the week. It will keep refrigerated up to 4 days.

GREEK PASTA SALAD

bacon, lettuce, and tomato pasta salad

SERVES 4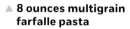

- ▲ **8 ounces multigrain farfalle pasta**
- ▲ **3 ripe plum tomatoes, chopped**
- ▲ **2 cups thinly sliced romaine lettuce**
- **3 slices cooked thick-cut bacon, crumbled**
- ▲ **¼ cup plain fat-free yogurt**
- **2 tablespoons fat-free mayonnaise**
- **2 tablespoons water**
- **1 tablespoon cider vinegar**
- **1 teaspoon sugar**
- **¼ teaspoon salt**
- **¼ teaspoon black pepper**

1 Cook pasta according to package directions, omitting salt. Rinse under cold water, drain, and transfer to large bowl.

2 Add tomatoes, lettuce, and bacon to bowl with pasta. Toss to combine. In small bowl, whisk together yogurt, mayonnaise, water, vinegar, sugar, salt, and pepper. Pour over pasta and toss to coat. Serve at once, or refrigerate up to 1 day.

Per serving (1 ¾ cups pasta salad): 271 Cal, 4 g Total Fat, 1 g Sat Fat, 0 g Trans Fat, 8 mg Chol, 366 mg Sod, 49 g Carb, 7 g Sugar, 3 g Fib, 12 g Prot, 55 mg Calc.

Stay On Track

To add more lean protein, stir 1 cup (4 ounces) diced cooked skinless turkey breast into the salad in step 2 and increase the per-serving **PointsPlus** value by **1**.

garlicky clam and sun-dried tomato pizza
SERVES 6

- ¼ cup sun-dried tomatoes (not packed in oil)
- 1 (10-ounce) prebaked whole wheat pizza crust
- 1 ¼ cups shredded fat-free mozzarella cheese
- 1 (6-ounce) can chopped clams, drained
- 3 cloves garlic, minced
- ⅛ teaspoon red pepper flakes
- 1 tablespoon grated Parmesan cheese
- ¼ cup fresh small basil leaves
- 2 teaspoons olive oil

1 Preheat oven to 450°F. Spray large baking sheet with nonstick spray.

2 Place sun-dried tomatoes in small bowl and cover with boiling water. Let stand until softened, about 10 minutes. Drain and coarsely chop.

3 Place pizza crust on prepared baking sheet. Sprinkle with mozzarella, leaving ½-inch border around edge. Top with sun-dried tomatoes and clams. Sprinkle with garlic, pepper flakes, and Parmesan. Bake until crust is browned and cheese is bubbling, 8–10 minutes. Sprinkle with basil and drizzle with oil. Cut into 6 pieces.

Per serving (1 piece pizza): 181 Cal, 3 g Total Fat, 0 g Sat Fat, 0 g Trans Fat, 10 mg Chol, 612 mg Sod, 24 g Carb, 1 g Sugar, 3 g Fib, 14 g Prot, 243 mg Calc.

MUSHROOM AND ARUGULA PIZZA p 128

GARLICKY CLAM AND SUN-DRIED TOMATO PIZZA p 125

mushroom and arugula pizza

SERVES 6

- 2 teaspoons cornmeal
- 1 pound thawed frozen whole wheat pizza dough
- 2 teaspoons olive oil
- 1 cup sliced shiitake mushroom caps
- ½ small onion, chopped
- 2 garlic cloves, minced
- ½ teaspoon dried thyme
- 1 (8-ounce) can no-salt-added pizza sauce
- ⅓ cup shredded part-skim mozzarella cheese
- 2 cups baby arugula
- 1 teaspoon balsamic vinegar
- Pinch black pepper

1 Spray large baking sheet with nonstick spray and sprinkle lightly with cornmeal.

2 Sprinkle work surface lightly with flour. With lightly floured rolling pin, roll dough into 12-inch round. Transfer round to prepared baking sheet, gently reshaping dough as necessary. Cover loosely with plastic wrap and let rise in warm spot 30 minutes.

3 Place rack on bottom rung of oven. Preheat oven to 450°F.

4 Meanwhile, heat 1 teaspoon oil in medium nonstick skillet over medium heat. Add mushrooms and onion; cook, stirring frequently, until vegetables soften, about 7 minutes. Stir in garlic and thyme. Spread sauce over dough. Top evenly with mozzarella and mushroom mixture. Bake until crust is browned and cheese is bubbling, 18–20 minutes.

5 Toss arugula, vinegar, pepper, and remaining 1 teaspoon oil in medium bowl. Slide pizza onto large cutting board. Top with arugula mixture and cut into 6 slices.

Per serving (1 slice): 241 Cal, 5 g Total Fat, 1 g Sat Fat, 0 g Trans Fat, 3 mg Chol, 361 mg Sod, 41 g Carb, 4 g Sugar, 5 g Fib, 8 g Prot, 95 mg Calc.

Stay On Track

Start your meal with an artichoke salad: Toss together 1 can artichoke hearts in brine, drained, rinsed, and chopped; 1 grated carrot; plenty of chopped fresh parsley; and a splash of red-wine vinegar.

three-cheese polenta pizza with fresh tomatoes

SERVES 4

- 1 (16-ounce) tube refrigerated fat-free plain polenta, cut into ¼-inch-thick slices

- ¾ cup part-skim ricotta cheese

- ¼ cup grated pecorino cheese

- ⅛ teaspoon red pepper flakes

- 1 tablespoon chopped fresh oregano or 1 teaspoon dried

- 2 plum tomatoes, thinly sliced and patted dry on paper towels

- ½ cup shredded part-skim mozzarella cheese

- 2 tablespoons thinly sliced fresh basil leaves

1 Preheat broiler. Spray 10-inch pizza pan or large baking sheet with nonstick spray.

2 Place 1 slice of polenta in center of prepared pan; arrange remaining slices in 2 concentric circles around first slice, overlapping slightly to form 10-inch round. Lightly spray polenta with nonstick spray. Broil polenta 4 inches from heat until lightly browned and heated through, 6–8 minutes.

3 Meanwhile, stir together ricotta, pecorino, pepper flakes, and oregano.

4 Arrange tomato slices on polenta. Top tomatoes with dollops of ricotta mixture; sprinkle with mozzarella. Broil until tomatoes are hot and mozzarella is melted, about 4 minutes. Sprinkle with basil. Cut into 4 wedges and serve at once.

Per serving (1 wedge): 241 Cal, 8 g Total Fat, 5 g Sat Fat, 0 g Trans Fat, 26 mg Chol, 676 mg Sod, 27 g Carb, 3 g Sugar, 2 g Fib, 14 g Prot, 473 mg Calc.

6

Chapter 5

easy roasts
& oven dinners

easy roasts
& oven dinners

sirloin spoon roast with gravy and thyme potatoes

SERVES 12

- ▲ **1 (3-pound) lean boneless top sirloin roast, trimmed and tied**
- **¾ teaspoon black pepper**
- **1 ¼ teaspoons salt**
- **4 shallots, sliced**
- ▲ **8 medium new potatoes (2 pounds), each cut into 6 wedges**
- **1 ½ teaspoons olive oil**
- ▲ **1 ¼ cups reduced-sodium beef broth**
- **3 garlic cloves, finely chopped**
- **1 tablespoon chopped fresh thyme**
- **2 teaspoons all-purpose flour**

1 Preheat oven to 450°F.

2 Sprinkle roast with pepper and 1 teaspoon salt. Scatter shallots evenly over bottom of large metal roasting pan. Place roast on top of shallots. Toss potatoes, oil, and remaining ¼ teaspoon salt on large rimmed baking sheet. Spread potatoes in single layer. Transfer beef and potatoes to oven and roast 20 minutes. Reduce oven temperature to 325°F. Pour ½ cup broth around beef. Continue to roast beef and potatoes, turning potatoes once or twice, until instant-read thermometer inserted into center of beef registers 145°F for medium, about 30 minutes longer. Transfer beef to cutting board and cover loosely with foil; let stand 15 minutes.

3 Sprinkle potatoes with garlic and thyme. Return to oven and roast, turning potatoes once or twice, until potatoes are very tender, about 10 minutes longer.

4 Meanwhile, to make gravy, set roasting pan with shallots over medium heat on stovetop. Stir in flour and cook, stirring, 1 minute. Whisk in remaining ¾ cup broth and bring to simmer. Simmer until sauce bubbles and thickens, about 3 minutes. Cut beef across grain into 12 slices and serve with potatoes and gravy.

Per serving (1 slice beef, 4 potato wedges, and 2 tablespoons gravy): 224 Cal, 6 g Total Fat, 2 g Sat Fat, 0 g Trans Fat, 49 mg Chol, 305 mg Sod, 15 g Carb, 2 g Sugar, 2 g Fib, 29 g Prot, 34 mg Calc.

BEEF TENDERLOIN WITH PARMESAN CRUST

CRISPY HASSELBACK YUKON POTATOES p 194

beef tenderloin with parmesan crust
SERVES 4

- 1 ½ pounds lean beef tenderloin, in 1 piece, trimmed and tied
- ¼ teaspoon salt
- ¼ teaspoon black pepper
- ¾ teaspoon canola oil
- ¼ cup grated Parmesan cheese
- ¼ cup finely chopped fresh parsley
- 1 tablespoon Dijon mustard
- 1 tablespoon reduced-fat mayonnaise
- 3 garlic cloves, minced

1 Preheat oven to 450°F. Position rack in top third of oven.

2 Sprinkle beef with salt and pepper. Heat oil in large ovenproof skillet over medium-high heat. Add beef and cook until browned on all sides, about 10 minutes. Remove beef from pan and set on cutting board.

3 Combine Parmesan, parsley, mustard, mayonnaise, and garlic in small bowl. Remove and discard string from tenderloin. Spread Parmesan mixture over top and sides of tenderloin; return to skillet. Transfer skillet to oven and roast until instant-read thermometer inserted into center of beef registers 145°F for medium, about 25 minutes. Transfer beef to cutting board and let stand 10 minutes. Cut into 8 slices.

Per serving (2 slices beef): 291 Cal, 13 g Total Fat, 5 g Sat Fat, 0 g Trans Fat, 105 mg Chol, 422 mg Sod, 3 g Carb, 0 g Sugar, 0 g Fib, 39 g Prot, 88 mg Calc.

Stay On Track
Steamed asparagus sprinkled with lemon and dill makes a simple but elegant side to this superb roast.

pork roast au poivre with fennel

SERVES 4

- 2 fennel bulbs, trimmed and thinly sliced, fronds reserved and chopped
- 2 tablespoons brandy
- 1 teaspoon olive oil
- 1 teaspoon coarse sea salt
- 2 teaspoons whole black peppercorns, crushed
- 1 teaspoon fennel seed, crushed
- 1 (1 ¼-pound) lean pork tenderloin, trimmed

1 Preheat oven to 400°F. Place sliced fennel in 9 x 13-inch baking dish and toss with brandy, oil, and ½ teaspoon salt.

2 Combine remaining ½ teaspoon salt, peppercorns, and fennel seed in small bowl; rub mixture over pork. Place pork in baking dish on top of fennel and roast until pork is browned and instant-read thermometer inserted into center registers 145°F for medium, 30–40 minutes.

3 Transfer pork to cutting board and let stand 10 minutes. Cut into 12 slices and sprinkle with fennel fronds. Serve with fennel mixture.

Per serving (3 slices pork and ½ cup fennel mixture): 222 Cal, 5 g Total Fat, 1 g Sat Fat, 0 g Trans Fat, 92 mg Chol, 651 mg Sod, 9 g Carb, 0 g Sugar, 4 g Fib, 31 g Prot, 73 mg Calc.

For Your Information

To trim a fennel bulb, remove the feathery fronds and any thick stalks that protrude from the bulb. (Reserve the fronds for garnish.) Cut about one-quarter inch off the bottom of the bulb; then cut lengthwise into thin slices.

herb roasted pork primavera
SERVES 6

2 teaspoons chopped fresh rosemary

2 teaspoons chopped fresh thyme

1 garlic clove, minced

½ teaspoon black pepper

¾ teaspoon salt

▲ 1 (1 ½-pound) piece lean boneless center-cut pork loin, trimmed

2 teaspoons olive oil

▲ 1 pound small red potatoes, halved

▲ 1 (9-ounce) package frozen artichoke hearts, thawed and patted dry

▲ 1 cup baby-cut carrots

1 Preheat oven to 450°F. Spray large shallow roasting pan with nonstick spray.

2 Stir together rosemary, thyme, garlic, pepper, and ¼ teaspoon salt in cup. Rub mixture all over pork. Heat 1 teaspoon oil in large skillet over medium-high heat. Add pork and cook until browned on all sides, about 5 minutes.

3 Transfer pork to prepared roasting pan. Toss potatoes, artichoke hearts, carrots, remaining 1 teaspoon oil, and remaining ½ teaspoon salt together in large bowl. Scatter vegetables around pork. Roast, stirring vegetables once or twice, until instant-read thermometer inserted into center of pork registers 145°F for medium and vegetables are tender, about 40 minutes. Transfer pork to cutting board and let stand 5 minutes. Cut pork into 12 slices and serve with vegetables.

Per serving (2 slices pork with 1 scant cup vegetables): 240 Cal, 8 g Total Fat, 2 g Sat Fat, 0 g Trans Fat, 66 mg Chol, 378 mg Sod, 18 g Carb, 2 g Sugar, 4 g Fib, 24 g Prot, 54 mg Calc.

Stay On Track

If you like, add 2 cups small whole cremini mushrooms to the vegetables in step 3.

mediterranean meat loaf with roast tomatoes

SERVES 6

- ¾ pound ground lean beef (7% fat or less)
- ¾ pound ground lean lamb
- ½ small onion, finely chopped
- ⅓ cup chopped pitted brine-cured black olives
- ⅓ cup seasoned dried whole wheat bread crumbs
- ¼ cup fat-free milk
- 3 tablespoons chopped fresh oregano
- ¾ teaspoon +⅛ teaspoon salt
- ½ teaspoon black pepper
- 6 plum tomatoes, halved lengthwise
- 3 garlic cloves, chopped
- ½ teaspoon olive oil

1 Preheat oven to 375°F. Line bottom of 9 x 13-inch baking pan with parchment paper.

2 Mix together beef, lamb, onion, olives, bread crumbs, milk, oregano, ¾ teaspoon salt, and pepper in large bowl until combined. Transfer mixture to prepared pan and shape into 5 x 11-inch loaf. Scatter tomatoes around meat loaf. Sprinkle tomatoes with garlic and remaining ⅛ teaspoon salt; drizzle with oil. Roast until instant-read thermometer inserted into center of meat loaf registers 160°F and tomatoes are softened and lightly browned, about 50 minutes. Let meat loaf stand 10 minutes. Cut into 6 slices and serve with tomatoes.

Per serving (1 slice meat loaf and 2 tomato halves): 205 Cal, 8 g Total Fat, 3 g Sat Fat, 0 g Trans Fat, 66 mg Chol, 545 mg Sod, 9 g Carb, 3 g Sugar, 2 g Fib, 23 g Prot, 66 mg Calc.

Stay On Track

If you like, roast a thinly sliced red onion along with the tomatoes and serve with a simple green salad tossed with a little lemon juice, salt, and pepper.

MEDITERRANEAN MEAT LOAF WITH ROAST TOMATOES

peruvian chicken with avocado and red onion salad

2 tablespoons white-wine vinegar

1 tablespoon paprika

1 tablespoon ground cumin

5 garlic cloves, minced

1 teaspoon canola oil

⅛ teaspoon cayenne

1 ¼ teaspoons salt

1 (3 ½-pound) whole chicken, skin and wings removed and discarded

▲ 1 heart of romaine lettuce, thinly sliced (6 cups)

▲ ½ small red onion, thinly sliced

½ small avocado, pitted, peeled, and thinly sliced

Juice of ½ lime

1 Preheat oven to 400°F. Spray roasting rack with nonstick spray and place in roasting pan.

2 Stir together vinegar, paprika, cumin, garlic, oil, cayenne, and 1 teaspoon salt in small bowl. Rub spice mixture all over meat and inside cavity of chicken. Tie legs together with kitchen string. Place chicken, breast side up, on prepared rack in pan. Roast until instant-read thermometer inserted into thigh (not touching bone) registers 165°F, about 1 hour. Transfer chicken to cutting board and let stand 10 minutes.

3 To make salad, combine romaine and onion on serving platter. Top with sliced avocado; sprinkle with lime juice and remaining ¼ teaspoon salt.

4 Carve chicken into 6 pieces and serve with salad.

Per serving (1 piece chicken and 1 cup salad): 200 Cal, 7 g Total Fat, 1 g Sat Fat, 0 g Trans Fat, 89 mg Chol, 591 mg Sod, 5 g Carb, 1 g Sugar, 3 g Fib, 29 g Prot, 49 mg Calc.

For Your Information

This recipe's combination of bright spices and just a touch of canola oil results in a delicious skinless roast bird. Just make sure you don't overcook it: Check the temperature 10 minutes before the end of the estimated cooking time.

crispy chicken fingers with sweet ginger sauce

SERVES 4

⅔ cup low-fat buttermilk

8 chicken breast tenders (about 1 ¼ pounds), cut lengthwise in half

3 cups cornflakes

2 tablespoons sesame seeds (brown or black, or a combination of both)

1 teaspoon salt

3 tablespoons apricot fruit spread

1 tablespoon reduced-sodium soy sauce

½ teaspoon grated peeled fresh ginger

2 tablespoons water

1 Pour buttermilk into medium bowl and add chicken. Cover and refrigerate at least 10 minutes or up to 8 hours.

2 Position rack in top third of oven; preheat oven to 425°F. Line large rimmed baking sheet with parchment paper.

3 Place cornflakes in large zip-close plastic bag. With rolling pin or meat mallet, finely crush cornflakes. Add sesame seeds and salt, and shake to combine.

4 With tongs, remove chicken, a few pieces at a time, from buttermilk, letting excess buttermilk drip back into bowl. Place chicken in bag with cornflake mixture. Shake bag to coat chicken; remove chicken and place on prepared baking sheet. Repeat with remaining chicken. Discard leftover buttermilk and cornflake mixture. Lightly spray chicken pieces with nonstick spray. Bake until chicken is crisp and cooked through, about 10 minutes.

5 Stir together fruit spread, soy sauce, ginger, and water. Serve with chicken.

Per serving (4 chicken fingers and 1 ½ tablespoons sauce): 263 Cal, 6 g Total Fat, 1 g Sat Fat, 0 g Trans Fat, 79 mg Chol, 708 mg Sod, 21 g Carb, 8 g Sugar, 1 g Fib, 31 g Prot, 40 mg Calc.

Make Ahead

You can freeze the chicken fingers to have on hand for future meals. Simply transfer the baked, cooled fingers to a zip-close plastic freezer bag, and freeze up to 3 months. Reheat in a 325°F oven until hot, 15 to 20 minutes.

ROASTING BASICS

Nothing beats an oven meal for filling your house with mouthwatering aromas and giving you meats and vegetables that are browned and caramelized outside while juicy and super flavorful inside. Better yet, most roasting recipes offer one-dish cleanup—the payoff of more time in the oven means less time doing dishes. Here are some essentials.

A good roasting pan is heavy enough to maintain even heat in the oven and should have sides 2- to 3-inches-high to allow air to circulate, but still protect your oven against splattering. Ideally, your pan should be made of material like steel or cast iron, so that it can go from the oven to the stove top for deglazing and making pan sauces.

For casseroles and smaller dinners, **having baking dishes in a few sizes** is convenient. Glass, ceramic, or glazed cast-iron are excellent options. Pans 8 x 8-inches and 9 x 13-inches are the most practical.

It's great to have a **rack that fits snuggly** in your roasting pan so that foods like chicken, meat, or turkey brown all over instead of steaming in their juices. If you don't have one, try laying carrots or celery stalks across the bottom of your pan to elevate the food.

A good thermometer is the best way to establish the proper degree of doneness for meats and poultry. We recommend an instant-read thermometer for ease of use, plus it's small enough to fit in an apron or shirt pocket.

To accurately measure temperatures, **always insert the thermometer into the center of the food;** make sure it is not touching bone if your roast has one. Follow the minimum safe cooking temperatures in the chart at right.

For easiest cleanup, line the bottom of your roasting pan with foil or parchment paper when it makes sense for your recipe. Also remember to get your pan soaking in soapy water as soon as possible after removing food so that baked-on residue can begin to soften.

MINIMUM SAFE COOKING TEMPERATURES

TYPE OF FOOD	TEMPERATURE FAHRENHEIT
GROUND BEEF, PORK, AND LAMB	160°
BEEF, LAMB, AND PORK STEAKS, CHOPS, AND ROASTS	145°
FRESH HAM	165°
FULLY COOKED HAM (TO REHEAT)	140°
CHICKEN OR TURKEY, WHOLE, PARTS, AND GROUND	165°
EGG DISHES	160°
LEFTOVERS AND CASSEROLES	165°

roast chicken and asparagus with mustard cream sauce

SERVES 4

4 (¼-pound) skinless boneless chicken thighs, trimmed

1 teaspoon dried thyme

¼ teaspoon black pepper

½ teaspoon salt

▲ 1 pound medium-thick asparagus, trimmed

1 teaspoon olive oil

⅓ cup dry white wine

▲ ⅓ cup reduced-sodium chicken broth

1 shallot, finely chopped

1 tablespoon light cream cheese (Neufchâtel)

2 ½ teaspoons coarse-grained mustard

1 Preheat oven to 375°F. Spray 9 x 13-inch baking pan with nonstick spray.

2 Sprinkle chicken with thyme, pepper, and ¼ teaspoon salt; place in prepared baking pan. Roast until chicken is cooked through, 25–30 minutes.

3 Meanwhile, place asparagus on large rimmed baking sheet and toss with oil and remaining ½ teaspoon salt. Arrange in single layer. Place in oven after chicken has cooked 20 minutes, and roast until bright green and crisp tender, about 10 minutes.

4 Combine wine, broth, and shallot in small saucepan. Bring to boil. Reduce heat and simmer until liquid is reduced by half, about 5 minutes. Add cream cheese and mustard, and stir until smooth.

5 Transfer chicken and asparagus to platter. Pour any pan juices from chicken into mustard sauce. Reheat sauce if necessary, and serve over chicken and asparagus.

Per serving (1 chicken thigh, 6 stalks asparagus, and **2 tablespoons sauce**): 235 Cal, 11 g Total Fat, 3 g Sat Fat, 0 g Trans Fat, 78 mg Chol, 444 mg Sod, 7 g Carb, 3 g Sugar, 2 g Fib, 24 g Prot, 56 mg Calc.

rosemary oven-fried chicken
SERVES 4

⅓ cup all-purpose flour

▲ 1 large egg

▲ ¼ cup fat-free milk

1 cup panko (bread crumbs)

3 tablespoons grated Parmesan cheese

1½ tablespoons very finely chopped fresh rosemary

¼ teaspoon salt

Pinch cayenne

8 (3 ½-ounce) skinless chicken drumsticks

1 Preheat oven to 425°F. Line shallow baking pan with foil. Place wire rack in pan. Spray rack with nonstick spray.

2 Place flour on sheet of wax paper. Whisk together egg and milk in shallow dish or pie plate until blended. Combine panko, Parmesan, rosemary, salt, and cayenne in another shallow bowl. Dip chicken, one piece at a time, into flour, then into egg mixture, then into panko, pressing to adhere. Place chicken on prepared rack.

3 Lightly spray top of chicken with nonstick spray. Bake until chicken is cooked through and crumbs are golden, 35–40 minutes.

Per serving (2 drumsticks): 298 Cal, 7 g Total Fat, 2 g Sat Fat, 0 g Trans Fat, 143 mg Chol, 352 mg Sod, 27 g Carb, 1 g Sugar, 3 g Fib, 31 g Prot, 82 mg Calc.

Stay On Track
You can round out the meal by serving the chicken with baked potatoes (a 5-ounce potato per person will increase the per-serving *PointsPlus* value by **3**) and steamed green beans sprinkled with lemon juice.

italian turkey roulade

SERVES 6

- ▲ **10 sun-dried tomato halves (not packed in oil)**
- ▲ **1 (1 ¾-pound) skinless boneless turkey breast half**
- **½ teaspoon salt**
- **½ teaspoon black pepper**
- **3 (¾-ounce) slices provolone cheese**
- ▲ **1 cup baby arugula**
- **12 basil leaves**
- **1 teaspoon olive oil**

1 Preheat oven to 400°F. Line small rimmed baking sheet with parchment paper.

2 Place tomatoes in small bowl and cover with boiling water; let stand 10 minutes. Drain, pat dry, and cut into thin strips.

3 Place turkey on cutting board with short edge facing you. Holding knife parallel to board and starting at one long side, cut three-quarters of the way through turkey breast and open up like a book. Place plastic wrap over turkey and with wooden mallet or rolling pin pound to ½-inch thickness. Remove plastic wrap and sprinkle turkey on both sides with salt and pepper. Layer provolone, arugula, basil, and tomatoes on top, leaving 1-inch border around edges. Starting from long side, roll up turkey jelly-roll fashion. Tie with kitchen string at 1-inch intervals. Secure ends with wooden toothpicks to enclose filling. Brush turkey roll with oil.

4 Place turkey on prepared baking sheet and roast until browned and instant-read thermometer inserted into center of turkey registers 165°F, 35–40 minutes. Transfer turkey to cutting board and let stand 10 minutes. Cut string and remove toothpicks. Cut turkey into 12 slices.

Per serving (2 slices): 195 Cal, 5 g Total Fat, 2 g Sat Fat, 0 g Trans Fat, 94 mg Chol, 412 mg Sod, 2 g Carb, 1 g Sugar, 1 g Fib, 35 g Prot, 105 mg Calc.

Make Ahead
If you like, assemble the roll through step 3, cover with plastic wrap, and refrigerate up to 1 day before roasting.

baked tilapia with grapes and olives

SERVES 4

- 1 teaspoon olive oil
- ▲ 4 (5-ounce) tilapia fillets
- ¼ teaspoon salt
- ¼ teaspoon black pepper
- ▲ 1 ½ cups seedless red grapes, halved
- ⅓ cup pitted brine-cured kalamata olives, halved
- ¼ cup chopped fresh parsley
- 4 lemon wedges

1 Preheat oven to 400°F. Coat 9 x 13-inch baking dish with ½ teaspoon oil.

2 Sprinkle tilapia with salt and pepper and place in prepared baking dish. Top with grapes and olives, and drizzle with remaining ½ teaspoon oil. Bake until tilapia is just opaque in center and grapes are soft, about 15 minutes.

3 Sprinkle with parsley and serve with lemon wedges.

Per serving (1 piece tilapia and ⅓ cup grape mixture): 247 Cal, 9 g Total Fat, 2 g Sat Fat, 0 g Trans Fat, 71 mg Chol, 569 mg Sod, 13 g Carb, 9 g Sugar, 1 g Fib, 29 g Prot, 33 mg Calc.

Make Ahead

If you like, assemble this dish the night or morning before you want to serve it; cover and refrigerate. When it's dinnertime, all you'll have to do is bake and garnish it.

MISO-GLAZED SALMON
WITH MUSHROOMS AND
BOK CHOY

miso-glazed salmon with mushrooms and bok choy

SERVES 4

2 tablespoons white miso

1 ½ teaspoons honey

2 tablespoons reduced-sodium soy sauce

▲ 4 (5-ounce) pieces skinless wild salmon fillet

▲ 4 baby bok choy, halved lengthwise

▲ ½ pound shiitake mushrooms, stemmed and sliced

1 tablespoon lemon juice

1 Preheat oven to 425°F. Line a small baking sheet with parchment paper.

2 Stir together miso, honey, and 1 tablespoon soy sauce in small bowl. Place salmon on prepared pan. Spoon miso mixture evenly over salmon. Bake until salmon is just opaque in center, about 15 minutes.

3 Meanwhile, place bok choy and mushrooms in bottom of large steamer basket; set in large skillet over 1 inch of boiling water. Cover tightly and steam until vegetables are tender, 6–8 minutes. Serve with salmon sprinkled with lemon juice and remaining 1 tablespoon soy sauce.

Per serving (1 piece salmon, 2 pieces bok choy, and ⅓ cup mushrooms): 300 Cal, 10 g Total Fat, 2 g Sat Fat, 0 g Trans Fat, 90 mg Chol, 645 mg Sod, 16 g Carb, 7 g Sugar, 4 g Fib, 36 g Prot, 22 mg Calc.

For Your Information
If you have a choice between purchasing wild salmon and farm-raised salmon, consider opting for wild: Although farm-raised salmon is usually the cheaper option, it can be higher in some contaminants than wild salmon. And wild salmon, fresh or canned, is lower in fat content and a Weight Watchers Power Food.

monkfish with citrus gremolata

SERVES 4

- 4 (6-ounce) pieces monkfish fillet
- ½ teaspoon salt
- ¼ teaspoon black pepper
- 2 plum tomatoes, chopped
- ½ teaspoon olive oil
- 2 tablespoons chopped fresh parsley
- 1 tablespoon grated orange zest
- 2 teaspoons grated lemon zest
- 1 garlic clove, minced
- Lemon wedges

1 Preheat oven to 450°F. Spray baking dish with nonstick spray.

2 Sprinkle monkfish with salt and pepper. Place monkfish in prepared baking dish and surround with tomatoes. Drizzle with oil. Roast until fish is just opaque in center, 10–12 minutes.

3 Meanwhile, to make gremolata, stir together parsley, orange zest, lemon zest, and garlic in small bowl. Divide fish and tomatoes among 4 plates. Sprinkle fish evenly with gremolata and serve with lemon wedges.

Per serving (1 piece fish and ⅓ cup tomato mixture): 144 Cal, 3 g Total Fat, 1 g Sat Fat, 0 g Trans Fat, 43 mg Chol, 324 mg Sod, 2 g Carb, 1 g Sugar, 1 g Fib, 25 g Prot, 25 mg Calc.

roasted shellfish with herb sauce

SERVES 4

- 1 ¼ pounds extra-large shrimp, shelled and deveined
- 1 dozen littleneck clams
- ½ pound snow crab or Alaskan king crab legs, cracked

1 tablespoon olive oil

4 garlic cloves, minced

⅓ cup fat-free mayonnaise

3 tablespoons chopped fresh parsley

2 tablespoons chopped fresh cilantro

2 tablespoons chopped fresh chives

Zest and juice of 1 lemon

½ teaspoon hot pepper sauce

2 tablespoons water

Pinch salt

1 Preheat oven to 450°F. Position oven rack in middle of oven.

2 Place shrimp, clams, and crab legs in single layer on rimmed baking sheet or in large shallow roasting pan. Drizzle with oil and sprinkle with garlic. Toss gently to coat. Roast until shrimp are just opaque in center, crab legs are cooked through, and clams begin to open, about 10 minutes. Discard any clams that do not open.

3 Meanwhile, combine mayonnaise, parsley, cilantro, chives, lemon zest and juice, pepper sauce, water, and salt in small bowl. Divide sauce among 4 small dipping bowls, or dollop onto 4 small lettuce leaves; serve along with shellfish.

Per serving (4 shrimp, 3 clams, 2 crab legs, and 2 ½ tablespoons sauce): 255 Cal, 6 g Total Fat, 1 g Sat Fat, 0 g Trans Fat, 255 mg Chol, 933 mg Sod, 8 g Carb, 3 g Sugar, 1 g Fib, 41 g Prot, 111 mg Calc.

For Your Information

To crack crab legs, use a large heavy knife to split open large sections of the leg; then pull the shell open to expose some of the flesh (this will help the meat absorb flavoring and cook more evenly).

**ROASTED SHELLFISH WITH
HERB SAUCE** p 151

sardinian stuffed eggplant

SERVES 4

- ▲ 2 (1 ¼-pound) Italian eggplants
- **2 teaspoons olive oil**
- ▲ **1 large onion, diced**
- **5 garlic cloves, sliced**
- ▲ **1 large green bell pepper, diced**
- **¼ teaspoon salt**
- ▲ **1 (8-ounce) can no-salt-added tomato sauce**
- **Pinch red pepper flakes**
- **½ cup sliced basil leaves**
- **¼ cup chopped fresh mint**
- **⅓ cup + 2 tablespoons seasoned dried whole wheat bread crumbs**
- ▲ **1 large egg, lightly beaten**
- **¼ cup grated pecorino Romano cheese**

1 Preheat oven to 350°F. Line rimmed baking sheet with parchment paper.

2 Halve eggplants lengthwise and use spoon to scoop out flesh, leaving shell about ⅓-inch thick all around. Place shells, cut side down, on paper towels to drain. Dice flesh and set aside.

3 To make filling, heat oil in large skillet over medium-high heat. Add onion and garlic, and cook, stirring frequently, until onion is golden, about 8 minutes. Stir in bell pepper, salt, and diced eggplant. Cook, stirring occasionally, until eggplant has released most of its liquid and is tender, about 10 minutes. Stir in tomato sauce and pepper flakes; simmer 2 minutes. Transfer to large bowl and cool 5 minutes. Stir in basil, mint, and ⅓ cup bread crumbs. Stir in egg.

4 Spray eggplant shells with nonstick spray and place, cut side up, on prepared baking sheet. Spoon filling evenly into shells; sprinkle tops with remaining 2 tablespoons bread crumbs and pecorino cheese. Bake until filling is hot and top is browned, about 35 minutes. Cool 5 minutes before serving.

Per serving (1 stuffed half): 241 Cal, 7 g Total Fat, 3 g Sat Fat, 0 g Trans Fat, 61 mg Chol, 451 mg Sod, 36 g Carb, 14 g Sugar, 13 g Fib, 11 g Prot, 195 mg Calc.

Make Ahead

You can fill the eggplant shells and refrigerate them, covered tightly in plastic wrap, up to 3 days before baking. If the eggplant goes into the oven cold, you may need to add 5 to 10 minutes to the baking time.

baked tofu teriyaki with daikon salad
SERVES 4

- 2 (14-ounce) packages firm tofu
- ⅓ cup reduced-sodium teriyaki sauce
- 4 garlic cloves, minced
- Pinch red pepper flakes
- 3 tablespoons rice vinegar
- 1 teaspoon honey
- ¼ teaspoon salt
- 1 (¾-pound) daikon radish, peeled and shredded
- 2 carrots, shredded
- 4 scallions, thinly sliced
- 1 teaspoon Asian (dark) sesame oil
- Soy sauce for serving (optional)

1 Drain tofu and place blocks on plate. Cover with another plate and weight with food can or other object of about 1 pound. Let stand 20 minutes to remove excess liquid. Pour off liquid and cut each tofu block into 6 (¾-inch-thick) slices. Combine teriyaki, garlic, and pepper flakes in shallow baking dish. Add tofu, turn to coat, and let marinate 20 minutes.

2 Preheat oven to 400°F. Line rimmed baking sheet with parchment paper.

3 Remove tofu from marinade and discard marinade. Place tofu in single layer on prepared baking sheet. Bake until lightly browned on top, 45–50 minutes.

4 Meanwhile, whisk together vinegar, honey, and salt in large bowl. Add daikon, carrots, and scallions, and toss to coat. Drizzle tofu with oil. Serve with salad and more soy sauce (if using).

Per serving (3 slices tofu, ½ teaspoon sesame oil, and ⅔ cup salad): 269 Cal, 14 g Total Fat, 0 g Sat Fat, 0 g Trans Fat, 0 mg Chol, 517 mg Sod, 17 g Carb, 5 g Sugar, 2 g Fib, 21 g Prot, 406 mg Calc.

Chapter 6

best casseroles

best casseroles

beef and vegetable potpie casserole
SERVES 6

2 teaspoons canola oil

▲ 1 pound lean beef top round, trimmed and cut into ¾-inch cubes

▲ 1 onion, chopped

▲ 2 celery stalks, chopped

2 tablespoons + 1 teaspoon all-purpose flour

▲ 2 ½ cups reduced-sodium beef broth

▲ ½ pound red new potatoes, cut into 1-inch chunks

▲ 1 cup baby-cut carrots, halved

1 tablespoon Worcestershire sauce

▲ 1 cup frozen peas

½ (15-ounce) package refrigerated pie crust

1 Preheat oven to 375°F. Spray 3-quart baking dish lightly with nonstick spray.

2 Heat 1 teaspoon oil in large skillet over medium-high heat. Add beef and cook, turning occasionally, until browned, about 6 minutes. Transfer to plate.

3 Add remaining 1 teaspoon oil to skillet and set over medium heat. Add onion and celery; cook, stirring occasionally, until vegetables are softened, about 5 minutes. Sprinkle with flour and cook, stirring constantly, 1 minute.

4 Return beef to skillet. Add broth, potatoes, carrots, and Worcestershire sauce; bring to boil. Reduce heat and simmer, covered, until mixture bubbles and thickens, about 5 minutes. Remove from heat; stir in peas. Pour into prepared baking dish.

5 Unroll pie crust. Place dough over filling, leaving 1-inch overhang. Trim off any excess. Fold overhang under and crimp edges. Cut 6 (½-inch) slits in top of dough with paring knife to allow steam to escape. Bake until crust is golden brown and filling is hot and bubbling, 35–40 minutes (if edges of crust begin to brown too quickly, cover them with foil). Let stand 10 minutes before serving.

Per serving (generous 1 cup): 347 Cal, 14 g Total Fat, 5 g Sat Fat, 0 g Trans Fat, 51 mg Chol, 323 mg Sod, 32 g Carb, 5 g Sugar, 3 g Fib, 24 g Prot, 35 mg Calc.

texas beef and cornbread casserole

SERVES 8

- ▲ **1 pound lean beef sirloin, trimmed and cut into ½-inch cubes**
- ▲ **1 onion, chopped**
- ▲ **1 green bell pepper, chopped**
- ▲ **2 (15 ½-ounce) cans no-salt-added pinto beans, rinsed and drained**
- ▲ **1 (14 ½-ounce) can no-salt-added petite-diced tomatoes**
- **½ cup ketchup**
- **1 tablespoon cider vinegar**
- **1 teaspoon honey mustard**
- **½ cup water**
- **1 (6½-ounce) package cornbread mix**
- ▲ **⅓ cup fat-free milk**
- **1 tablespoon canola oil**

1 Preheat oven to 400°F.

2 Spray 3-quart flameproof casserole dish with lid with nonstick spray and set over medium-high heat. Add beef and cook, turning occasionally, until browned, about 6 minutes. Transfer to plate.

3 Add onion and bell pepper to casserole dish. Reduce heat to medium and cook, stirring frequently, until vegetables are softened, about 8 minutes. Stir in beef, beans, tomatoes, ketchup, vinegar, mustard, and water; bring to boil. Cover and bake 30 minutes.

4 Meanwhile, to make topping, combine cornbread mix, milk, and oil in small bowl; stir just until moistened (batter will be lumpy). Spoon batter by heaping tablespoonfuls over filling, making 8 mounds. Return casserole to oven and bake, uncovered, until cornbread is golden, about 15 minutes. Cool casserole 5 minutes before serving.

Per serving (⅔ cup beef mixture and 1 cornbread mound): 307 Cal, 7 g Total Fat, 2 g Sat Fat, 0 g Trans Fat, 25 mg Chol, 509 mg Sod, 40 g Carb, 10 g Sugar, 7 g Fib, 20 g Prot, 77 mg Calc.

Stay On Track

A crunchy salad of cucumber, tomatoes, and cilantro tossed with lime juice and a sprinkle of salt makes a refreshing accompaniment to this casserole.

TEXAS BEEF AND
CORNBREAD CASSEROLE

baked pork chops with apple stuffing

SERVES 4

- ▲ 4 (¼-pound) lean boneless center-cut pork loin chops, trimmed
- ½ teaspoon salt
- 2 teaspoons canola oil
- ▲ 1 onion, chopped
- ▲ 1 Granny Smith apple, cored and diced
- ▲ 2 celery stalks, chopped
- ¼ cup dried cranberries
- 2 garlic cloves, minced
- ▲ ¾ cup reduced-sodium chicken broth
- 2 slices whole wheat bread, crusts removed, bread cut into ½-inch cubes
- 1 tablespoon chopped fresh sage or 1 teaspoon dried

1 Preheat oven to 375°F. Spray shallow 1-quart baking dish with nonstick spray.

2 Sprinkle pork with ¼ teaspoon salt. Spray large skillet with nonstick spray and set over medium-high heat. Add pork and cook until browned, about 2 minutes per side. Transfer to prepared baking dish.

3 To make stuffing, heat oil in same skillet over medium-high heat. Add onion, apple, celery, cranberries, and garlic to skillet. Cook, stirring occasionally, until apple and vegetables soften, about 5 minutes. Add ¼ cup broth and bring to boil. Cook, stirring occasionally, until broth is almost evaporated and onion mixture is very tender, about 2 minutes. Transfer to large bowl. Add bread, sage, ¼ cup broth, and remaining ¼ teaspoon salt; toss to combine.

4 Top each pork chop with one-fourth of stuffing. Drizzle remaining ¼ cup broth around pork. Bake, uncovered, until instant-read thermometer inserted into side of a chop registers 145°F and stuffing is browned on top, about 20 minutes.

Per serving (1 pork chop with about ¼ cup stuffing): 261 Cal, 8 g Total Fat, 2 g Sat Fat, 0 g Trans Fat, 66 mg Chol, 445 mg Sod, 24 g Carb, 14 g Sugar, 3 g Fib, 24 g Prot, 64 mg Calc.

Make Ahead

If you like, you can make the stuffing in step 3 up to 2 days ahead. Place it in an airtight container and refrigerate until you're ready to assemble the casserole.

pork and savoy cabbage casserole
SERVES 6

- 1 (2 ½-pound) head Savoy cabbage
- 1 pound ground lean pork
- 1 large carrot, shredded
- 1 small onion, finely chopped
- ½ cup quick-cooking brown rice
- 1 large egg, lightly beaten
- ¼ teaspoon salt
- 1 ¼ cups reduced-sodium chicken broth
- 1 (24-ounce) jar no-salt-added marinara sauce
- 3 tablespoons red-wine vinegar
- 3 tablespoons golden raisins, chopped

1 Preheat oven to 350°F.

2 Bring large pot of water to boil. Core cabbage and carefully remove 12 outer leaves. Add cabbage leaves, 6 at a time, to pot and cook until wilted, about 2 minutes. Using tongs, transfer leaves to colander. Rinse under cold running water; set aside.

3 Cut remaining cabbage in half and add to pot; cook until tender, about 5 minutes. Drain and rinse under cold running water; drain again. Finely chop.

4 Spray 2 ½-quart round ovenproof casserole or soufflé dish with nonstick spray. Place 1 cabbage leaf in bottom of casserole. Arrange 9 cabbage leaves, rib ends up, around side of casserole, overlapping to cover inside of casserole and extending about 1 inch over rim. Reserve remaining 2 leaves for top.

5 Stir together pork, carrot, onion, rice, egg, salt, ¼ cup of broth, ½ cup of marinara sauce, and chopped cabbage in large bowl until combined. Spoon mixture into casserole. Fold cabbage leaves over filling and cover with reserved cabbage leaves. Pour remaining 1 cup broth around side of casserole. Bake 1 hour 15 minutes. Let stand 15 minutes.

6 Meanwhile, to make sauce, combine remaining marinara sauce, vinegar, and raisins in small saucepan. Simmer, uncovered, until slightly thickened, 8–10 minutes.

7 Carefully pour off and reserve broth from casserole. Place large plate over casserole and invert. Remove baking dish and cut casserole into 6 wedges. Serve with broth and sauce.

Per serving (1 wedge casserole and ⅓ cup sauce): 254 Cal, 6 g Total Fat, 2 g Sat Fat, 0 g Trans Fat, 80 mg Chol, 307 mg Sod, 30 g Carb, 14 g Sugar, 8 g Fib, 22 g Prot, 115 mg Calc.

tuscan lamb casserole with rosemary gremolata

SERVES 4

4 (6-ounce) lean lamb shanks, trimmed

¼ teaspoon salt

▲ **1 onion, finely chopped**

▲ **3 celery stalks, finely chopped**

▲ **1 (14 ½-ounce) can no-salt-added petite-diced tomatoes**

½ cup dry red wine

10 brine-cured kalamata olives, pitted and chopped

½ cup water

▲ **1 (15 ½-ounce) can no-salt-added navy beans, rinsed and drained**

Grated zest of 1 lemon

1 tablespoon chopped fresh rosemary

1 garlic clove, minced

1 Sprinkle lamb shanks with salt. Spray Dutch oven with nonstick spray and place over medium-high heat. Add lamb and cook until browned on all sides, about 8 minutes. Transfer to plate.

2 Preheat oven to 350°F.

3 Spray Dutch oven again with nonstick spray. Add onion and celery; cook, stirring frequently, until softened, about 6 minutes. Return lamb to Dutch oven. Add tomatoes, wine, olives, and water; bring to boil. Cover and bake until lamb is tender, about 1 hour 20 minutes. Stir in beans and continue to bake, covered, until beans are heated through and lamb is fork-tender, about 10 minutes longer.

4 Meanwhile to make gremolata, combine lemon zest, rosemary, and garlic in small bowl. Sprinkle over lamb casserole.

Per serving (1 shank with ¾ cup beans and sauce):
388 Cal, 9 g Total Fat, 3 g Sat Fat, 0 g Trans Fat, 114 mg Chol, 455 mg Sod, 29 g Carb, 6 g Sugar, 9 g Fib, 43 g Prot, 134 mg Calc.

easy chicken parmesan with basil
SERVES 4

¾ cup low-fat buttermilk

▲ 1 large egg white

⅔ cup whole wheat panko
(Japanese bread crumbs)

▲ 4 (5-ounce) skinless
boneless chicken breasts

¼ teaspoon salt

1 cup fat-free marinara
sauce

8 basil leaves

4 (½-ounce) slices
part-skim mozzarella
cheese

¼ cup chopped fresh basil

1 tablespoon grated
Parmesan cheese

1 Preheat oven to 425°F. Spray 7 x 11-inch baking dish with nonstick spray.

2 Whisk together buttermilk and egg white in shallow bowl or pie plate. Place panko on sheet of wax paper. Sprinkle chicken with salt. Dip chicken, one piece at a time, into buttermilk mixture, then coat with panko, pressing to adhere.

3 Place chicken in prepared baking dish and lightly spray chicken with nonstick spray. Bake until lightly browned, about 10 minutes; do not turn. Top each breast with 2 tablespoons marinara sauce, 2 basil leaves, and 1 slice mozzarella. Pour remaining ½ cup marinara sauce around chicken; bake until chicken is cooked through and cheese has melted, about 5 minutes longer. Serve topped with chopped basil and sprinkled with Parmesan.

Per serving (1 chicken breast and ¾ teaspoon Parmesan): 304 Cal, 7 g Total Fat, 3 g Sat Fat, 0 g Trans Fat, 88 mg Chol, 643 mg Sod, 19 g Carb, 2 g Sugar, 3 g Fib, 39 g Prot, 189 mg Calc.

Stay On Track
Serve each chicken breast with ½ cup cooked whole wheat spaghetti for an additional **2 PointsPlus** values per serving. And stir-fry zucchini chunks with a little nonstick spray, chopped chives, salt and pepper as a filling accompaniment.

**EASY CHICKEN PARMESAN
WITH BASIL** p 165

slow-cooker chicken fricassee casserole

SERVES 4

4 (¼-pound) skinless boneless chicken thighs, trimmed

▲ **½ pound cremini mushrooms, halved**

▲ **2 medium leeks, sliced and rinsed well, white and light-green parts only**

▲ **2 carrots, chopped**

▲ **1 small tomato, chopped**

▲ **2 cups reduced-sodium chicken broth**

2 tablespoons water

1 tablespoon all-purpose flour

¾ cup low-fat buttermilk baking mix

1 tablespoon chopped fresh dill

▲ **¼ cup fat-free milk**

1 Spray large skillet with nonstick spray and set over medium-high heat. Add chicken and cook until browned, turning once, about 5 minutes. Transfer chicken to slow cooker.

2 Add mushrooms, leeks, carrots, tomato, and broth to slow cooker. Cover and cook until chicken and vegetables are tender, 3–4 hours on high or 6–8 hours on low.

3 About 45 minutes before end of cooking time, whisk water and flour in small bowl until smooth. Stir flour mixture into slow cooker. Turn slow cooker to high if on low; cover and cook until mixture simmers and thickens, about 15 minutes.

4 Meanwhile, combine baking mix and dill in medium bowl. Add milk and stir just until soft dough forms. Drop dough onto simmering stew, making 4 dumplings. Cover and cook until toothpick inserted into center of dumpling comes out clean, about 30 minutes.

Per serving (1 ¼ cups casserole with 1 dumpling): 394 Cal, 12 g Total Fat, 3 g Sat Fat, 0 g Trans Fat, 75 mg Chol, 642 mg Sod, 43 g Carb, 9 g Sugar, 3 g Fib, 27 g Prot, 142 mg Calc.

Stay On Track
If you like, you can add 1 large diced bell pepper to the fricassee along with the vegetables in step 2.

paella-style chicken-and-chorizo casserole

SERVES 6

4 (¼-pound) skinless boneless chicken thighs, trimmed and cut into 2-inch pieces

2 teaspoons smoked paprika

½ teaspoon dried oregano

2 ounces chorizo sausage, thinly sliced

1 teaspoon olive oil

1 onion, thinly sliced

2 garlic cloves, minced

¾ cup brown rice

1 (14 ½-ounce) can fire-roasted diced tomatoes with green chiles

1½ cups reduced-sodium chicken broth

¼ cup small pimiento-stuffed green olives, halved

1 Preheat oven to 350°F.

2 Sprinkle chicken with paprika and oregano. Spray 3-quart Dutch oven with nonstick spray and set over medium-high heat. Add chicken and chorizo; cook, turning occasionally, until browned, about 5 minutes. Transfer chicken and chorizo to plate.

3 Add oil, onion, and garlic to Dutch oven; cook, stirring occasionally, until onion softens, about 5 minutes. Stir in rice, stirring until grains are coated. Return chicken and chorizo to Dutch oven. Add tomatoes, broth, and olives; bring to boil. Remove from heat. Cover and bake until liquid is absorbed and rice is tender, about 1 hour 10 minutes.

Per serving (1 cup): 288 Cal, 11 g Total Fat, 3 g Sat Fat, 0 g Trans Fat, 58 mg Chol, 299 mg Sod, 26 g Carb, 3 g Sugar, 3 g Fib, 20 g Prot, 40 mg Calc.

COZY UP TO FREEZING

In addition to saving you time and money, a full freezer can be one of your best allies in weight loss. Not only does it help you preserve the freshness of your favorite foods, but freezing leftovers also gets food out of the way, reducing the temptation to eat more than you planned. Follow these recommendations for making the most of your homemade meals and goodies; also see the chart on page 41 for information on recommended storage times.

FREEZING LEFTOVERS

Choose the correct containers. Plastic or glass containers designed especially for freezing are the best. Other containers can become brittle and crack, ruining your food.

Use freezer wraps. Use freezer-safe plastic wrap, heavy-duty foil, and freezer bags for best results. They will help prevent freezer burn (the result of loss of moisture) and protect against flavor change. This is particularly important for foods you plan to store for more than a week or two.

Allow foods to cool. Always let hot foods come to room temperature before freezing. Once cool to the touch, freeze your food immediately to prevent the growth of bacteria.

Label your foods. In a few weeks, you might have no idea what's in that frosty container or foil-wrapped bundle. Use an indelible marker and freezer tape to mark the date and contents. Add the serving size and *PointsPlus* value for easy tracking.

Keep it stocked. A full freezer operates more efficiently, so keep it filled with your favorite foods and save energy.

What not to freeze. A few foods will not respond well to freezing. Leftovers containing dairy items like milk, sour cream, yogurt, and cottage cheese may separate, and eggs may become rubbery. Some raw vegetables will become soggy and unappealing after freezing, such as lettuce, tomatoes, radishes, and cucumbers.

SAFE DEFROSTING

How you defrost your food is just as important as how you freeze it. Not only can improper thawing adversely affect the flavor and quality of your food, it can even be dangerous. In particular, never thaw foods on the counter at room temperature where bacteria can grow.

Refrigerator method. Experts agree: From both a quality and a safety standpoint, it's always best to thaw foods in the refrigerator. Plan ahead, and transfer foods from the freezer to your fridge 1 to 3 days in advance of using. Always place a plate or a dish underneath thawing foods to catch drips. Keep these guidelines in mind: 1 pound of frozen food will take about 24 hours to thaw, a 4-pound chicken will take 2 to 3 days to thaw, a 12-pound turkey will require 3 to 4 days, and a 9 x13-inch casserole will take 1 to 2 days. If, however, you find yourself in a race against the clock, you can use one of the following quick defrosting methods.

Cold-water method. Seal the wrapped frozen food in a zip-close plastic bag and immerse it in a large bowl or pot of cold water (never use warm water). Change the water every 30 minutes until the food is pliable, 1 to 2 hours per pound.

Microwave method. Remove food from the freezer wrap and transfer to a microwavable bowl or plate. Follow your microwave manufacturer's defrosting directions—for most microwave ovens, the rule is 7 to 10 minutes per pound on the defrost setting (50 percent power). Note that defrosting seafood in the microwave is not recommended, as it adversely affects its texture. And remember that microwave-thawed food must be cooked immediately to avoid possible bacterial growth.

hearty turkey moussaka

SERVES 6

- ½ eggplant, cut into 6 (½-inch-thick) rounds
- 1 zucchini, cut diagonally into 12 (¼-inch-thick) slices
- 2 teaspoons olive oil
- 1 pound ground skinless turkey breast
- 3 garlic cloves, minced
- 2 cups fat-free marinara sauce
- 1 teaspoon cinnamon
- 1 ⅓ cups plain fat-free Greek yogurt
- ⅓ cup grated Parmesan cheese
- 1 large egg
- 1 large egg white
- ¼ teaspoon ground allspice

1 Spray large baking sheet with nonstick spray; preheat broiler. Lightly spray both sides of eggplant and zucchini slices with nonstick spray. Place in single layer on prepared baking sheet. Broil 5 inches from heat, turning once, until lightly browned, about 10 minutes.

2 Preheat oven to 375°F. Spray 9 x 13-inch baking dish with nonstick spray.

3 Heat oil in large skillet over medium-high heat. Add turkey and garlic; cook, breaking turkey apart with spoon, until browned, about 5 minutes. Stir in marinara sauce and cinnamon; bring to boil. Reduce heat and simmer, stirring occasionally, until sauce thickens slightly, about 10 minutes.

3 Whisk together yogurt, Parmesan, egg, egg white, and allspice in small bowl.

4 Place eggplant in bottom of prepared baking dish; top with turkey mixture and spread evenly. Layer zucchini over turkey mixture. Top with yogurt mixture and spread evenly. Bake until center is hot and edges are bubbling, 35–40 minutes. Cool 15 minutes before serving.

Per serving (⅙ of moussaka): 216 Cal, 5 g Total Fat, 1 g Sat Fat, 0 g Trans Fat, 70 mg Chol, 474 mg Sod, 14 g Carb, 4 g Sugar, 4 g Fib, 29 g Prot, 129 mg Calc.

For Your Information

The Greek casserole known as moussaka is traditionally made with a heavy white sauce. Our version preserves the flavor profile, but lightens it with a yogurt-based sauce and lean turkey instead of ground lamb.

savory bread pudding with sausage and gruyère

SERVES 4

△ **1 cup fat-free milk**

△ **1 large egg**

△ **1 large egg white**

1 teaspoon dried sage

4 slices whole wheat sourdough bread, cut into 1-inch squares

6 ounces sweet Italian-style turkey sausage, casings removed

△ **1 cup grape tomatoes, halved**

2 tablespoons chopped fresh parsley

¾ cup shredded Gruyère cheese

1 Preheat oven to 375°F. Spray 7 x 11-inch baking dish with nonstick spray.

2 Whisk together milk, egg, egg white, and sage in large bowl. Add bread and let mixture stand, stirring occasionally, until bread absorbs some of liquid, about 10 minutes.

3 Meanwhile, spray medium skillet with nonstick spray and set over medium-high heat. Add sausage. Cook, breaking sausage apart with wooden spoon, until sausage is no longer pink, about 6 minutes. Transfer to plate. Add tomatoes to skillet; cook, stirring often, until softened, about 5 minutes. Stir sausage and tomatoes into bread mixture. Stir in parsley. Transfer to prepared baking dish. Sprinkle with Gruyère.

4 Bake until edges of pudding are browned, about 30 minutes. Serve at once.

Per serving (¼ of pudding): 292 Cal, 13 g Total Fat, 4 g Sat Fat, 0 g Trans Fat, 104 mg Chol, 643 mg Sod, 21 g Total Carb, 7 g Total Sugar, 3 g Fib, 20 g Prot, 220 mg Calc.

Make Ahead

You can assemble the pudding through step 3, cover with plastic wrap, and refrigerate up to 2 days. Bake as directed in step 4. Add 5 to 10 minutes to the baking time since the pudding will be going into the oven cold.

baked cod with potatoes, lemon, and capers

SERVES 4

- **3 medium Yukon Gold potatoes, each cut into 4 wedges**
- **1 tablespoon capers**
- **½ teaspoon smoked paprika**
- **2 tablespoons chopped fresh parsley**
- **1 ½ teaspoons olive oil**
- **¾ teaspoon salt**
- **Zest and juice of 1 lemon**
- **2 garlic cloves, minced**
- **4 (5-ounce) pieces skinless cod fillet**

1 Preheat oven to 425°F. Spray 9 x 13-inch baking dish with nonstick spray.

2 Put potatoes in large saucepan with enough water to cover by 2 inches. Bring to boil over high heat. Reduce heat and simmer until potatoes are translucent but centers are still firm, about 10 minutes; drain. Return potatoes to saucepan and add capers, paprika, 1 tablespoon parsley, 1 teaspoon oil, and ¼ teaspoon salt; toss gently to coat.

3 Combine lemon zest, garlic, remaining 1 tablespoon parsley, remaining ½ teaspoon oil, and remaining ½ teaspoon salt in small bowl. Rub herb mixture on both sides of cod. Lay cod in center of baking dish. Scatter potatoes around cod. Sprinkle cod and potatoes with lemon juice. Bake until fish is just opaque in center, about 12 minutes.

Per serving (1 cod fillet with ½ cup potatoes): 201 Cal, 3 g Total Fat, 0 g Sat Fat, 0 g Trans Fat, 54 mg Chol, 286 mg Sod, 22 g Carb, 3 g Sugar, 3 g Fib, 26 g Prot, 40 mg Calc.

For Your Information

Cod is a classic for Mediterranean-inspired fish dishes like this one, but you can also substitute any thick, white, skinless fillet, such as halibut or sea bass.

BAKED COD WITH
POTATOES, LEMON,
AND CAPERS

individual tuna noodle casseroles with mushrooms

SERVES 4

2 teaspoons canola oil

▲ 1 (8-ounce) package cremini mushrooms, sliced

2 shallots, thinly sliced

2 tablespoons all-purpose flour

▲ 2 ½ cups fat-free milk

½ cup fat-free mayonnaise

Pinch cayenne

▲ 1 cup frozen peas

▲ 2 cups cooked wide whole wheat egg noodles

▲ 1 (12-ounce) can solid white tuna in water, drained and flaked

1 cup reduced-fat baked potato chips, coarsely crushed

1 Preheat oven to 350°F. Spray 4 (8-ounce) ramekins or custard cups with nonstick spray.

2 To make sauce, heat oil in large skillet over medium-high heat. Add mushrooms and shallots, and cook, stirring frequently, until mushrooms are tender, about 8 minutes. Sprinkle flour over mushroom mixture; cook, stirring, 2 minutes. Gradually stir in milk, mayonnaise, and cayenne; bring to simmer. Reduce heat to medium-low and cook, stirring occasionally, until mixture bubbles and thickens, about 3 minutes. Stir in peas and cook 1 minute. Remove sauce from heat.

3 Add noodles and tuna to sauce, and stir to combine. Divide mixture evenly among prepared ramekins. Scatter potato chips evenly on top. Bake until filling is bubbling and top is golden, about 25 minutes.

Per serving (1 ramekin): 276 Cal, 6 g Total Fat, 1 g Sat Fat, 0 g Trans Fat, 28 mg Chol, 512 mg Sod, 34 g Carb, 10 g Sugar, 4 g Fib, 23 g Prot, 163 mg Calc.

Make Ahead

These casseroles are convenient to have on hand for quick lunches or dinners. Let cool, cover and refrigerate up to 3 days. Reheat them, uncovered, in a 300°F oven for 20 minutes, or microwave for 3 to 5 minutes.

eggplant, zucchini, and white bean gratin

SERVES 4

3 teaspoons olive oil

▲ **1 onion, finely chopped**

▲ **1 (1-pound) eggplant, cut into 1-inch pieces**

▲ **1 zucchini, cut into 1-inch pieces**

▲ **¼ cup reduced-sodium chicken or vegetable broth**

▲ **½ head escarole, cleaned and chopped**

▲ **1 (15 ½-ounce) can no-salt-added cannellini beans, rinsed and drained**

▲ **1 (14 ½-ounce) can stewed tomatoes**

¼ cup dried whole wheat bread crumbs

Grated zest of 1 lemon

1 garlic clove, minced

½ cup chopped fresh basil

1 Preheat oven to 375°F.

2 Heat 2 teaspoons oil in 3-quart flameproof casserole dish over medium heat. Add onion and cook, stirring occasionally, until softened, about 5 minutes. Add eggplant, zucchini, and broth. Cover and cook, stirring occasionally, until vegetables are tender, about 8 minutes. Uncover and cook, stirring, until vegetables begin to brown, about 5 minutes. Add escarole, beans, and tomatoes; bring to boil. Reduce heat; cover and simmer, stirring occasionally, until escarole is tender, about 10 minutes.

3 Combine bread crumbs, lemon zest, garlic, and remaining 1 teaspoon oil in small bowl. Sprinkle over top of vegetable mixture. Bake until gratin is hot and topping is browned, about 25 minutes. Sprinkle with basil.

Per serving (1 ½ cups): 232 Cal, 5 g Total Fat, 1 g Sat Fat, 0 g Trans Fat, 0 mg Chol, 367 mg Sod, 39 g Carb, 11 g Sugar, 13 g Fib, 10 g Prot, 162 mg Calc.

For Your Information

Using unpeeled eggplant and squash in this recipe adds color, flavor, and fiber, and also helps to maintain the shape of the vegetables during cooking.

tempeh-quinoa stuffed bell peppers

SERVES 4

- 4 large red bell peppers, stems intact
- 1 teaspoon olive oil
- 1 red onion, chopped
- 3 garlic cloves, minced
- 3 cups tightly packed baby spinach
- ½ teaspoon dried oregano
- 8 ounces tempeh, crumbled
- 1 cup cooked quinoa
- ⅓ cup crumbled fat-free feta cheese
- 2 tablespoons pine nuts, toasted
- ¼ teaspoon salt
- ¼ teaspoon black pepper
- 1 cup drained no-salt-added petite-diced tomatoes

1 Preheat oven to 375°F. Spray small, deep casserole dish or 1 ½-quart soufflé dish with nonstick spray.

2 From each bell pepper slice off top ½ inch from stem end and reserve. Remove ribs and seeds. Stand peppers on plate and cover with wax paper. Microwave on High until slightly softened, about 3 minutes; let cool covered with wax paper. Meanwhile, place tops of peppers on another plate, cover with wax paper and microwave on High until slightly softened, about 2 minutes; let cool covered with wax paper.

3 Heat oil in large skillet over medium heat. Add onion and garlic; cook, stirring occasionally, until onion is softened, about 5 minutes. Add spinach and oregano. Cook, stirring constantly, until spinach is wilted and liquid has evaporated, about 2 minutes. Remove from heat and stir in tempeh, quinoa, feta, pine nuts, salt, black pepper, and ½ cup tomatoes.

4 Fill bell peppers evenly with stuffing. Place peppers in prepared casserole dish and cap each with a pepper top. Pour remaining ½ cup tomatoes around peppers. Bake until peppers are very tender and stuffing is heated through, about 30 minutes.

Per serving (1 stuffed pepper): 303 Cal, 12 g Total Fat, 2 g Sat Fat, 0 g Trans Fat, 1 mg Chol, 283 mg Sod, 34 g Carb, 10 g Sugar, 7 g Fib, 18 g Prot, 151 mg Calc.

**TEMPEH-QUINOA STUFFED
BELL PEPPERS**

two-bean and cheese enchiladas with salsa verde

SERVES 4

2 teaspoons olive oil

▲ **1 onion, finely chopped**

▲ **1 red bell pepper, finely chopped**

2 garlic cloves, minced

1 teaspoon ground cumin

¼ cup water

▲ **1 (15 ½-ounce) can no-salt-added black beans, rinsed and drained**

▲ **1 cup fat-free refried beans**

1 chipotle en adobo + 2 tablespoons adobo sauce

▲ **1 (16-ounce) jar reduced-sodium fat-free salsa verde**

8 (6-inch) corn tortillas

▲ **½ cup shredded fat-free Cheddar cheese**

1 Preheat oven to 350°F.

2 Heat oil in medium skillet over medium heat. Add onion, bell pepper, garlic, and cumin. Cook, stirring occasionally, until vegetables soften, about 5 minutes. Add water and bring to boil. Reduce heat and simmer, covered, until vegetables are tender, about 3 minutes longer. Stir in black beans, refried beans, chipotle en adobo, and adobo sauce. Remove from heat.

3 Spread ½ cup salsa over bottom of 9 x 13-inch baking dish. Place 1 tortilla on work surface and top with ¼ cup bean mixture. Fold over two opposite sides of tortilla to enclose filling. Place seam side down in baking dish. Repeat with remaining tortillas and bean mixture, making 8 enchiladas. Pour remaining salsa over enchiladas.

4 Spray sheet of foil with nonstick spray and cover baking dish, sprayed side down. Bake 20 minutes. Remove foil. Sprinkle with Cheddar and bake until edges of enchiladas begin to brown and cheese has melted, about 15 minutes longer. Cool 10 minutes before serving.

Per serving (2 enchiladas): 385 Cal, 5 g Total Fat, 0 g Sat Fat, 0 g Trans Fat, 3 mg Chol, 964 mg Sod, 67 g Carb, 8 g Sugar, 12 g Fib, 16 g Prot, 215 mg Calc.

For Your Information

If you're using tortillas that have been frozen or refrigerated, you'll want to soften them before filling and folding them. Simply stack the tortillas between damp paper towels and microwave on High until heated through, about 30 seconds.

italian vegetable casserole with cranberry beans

SERVES 6

- 1 (15 ½-ounce) can cranberry beans, rinsed and drained
- 1 (14 ½-ounce) can diced tomatoes
- 1 (10-ounce) box frozen corn kernels
- 1 zucchini, chopped
- 1 cup thawed peeled frozen fava beans

1 cup fat-free marinara sauce

1 garlic clove, chopped

2 teaspoons Italian seasoning

- 1 (16-ounce) tube prepared fat-free polenta, cut into 12 (½-inch) slices

1 cup shredded reduced-fat Italian cheese blend

1 Preheat oven to 400°F. Spray shallow 2 ½-quart baking dish with nonstick spray.

2 Combine cranberry beans, tomatoes, corn, zucchini, fava beans, marinara, garlic, and Italian seasoning in large saucepan. Place over high heat and bring to boil. Reduce heat and simmer, covered, 10 minutes. Transfer mixture to baking dish. Arrange polenta slices on top, overlapping slices if needed.

3 Bake until bubbly at edges, about 25 minutes. Sprinkle polenta with cheese blend and continue to bake until cheese melts, about 5 minutes. Let stand 10 minutes before serving.

Per serving (⅙ of casserole): 310 Cal, 5 g Total Fat, 2 g Sat Fat, 0 g Trans Fat, 10 mg Chol, 969 mg Sod, 51 g Carb, 5 g Sugar, 8 g Fib, 15 g Prot, 448 mg Calc.

For Your Information

If you can't find frozen fava beans, frozen shelled edamame or baby lima beans are a good substitute. If you do use favas, remember that they are often frozen with their tough, whitish outer skin intact, which should be removed before you use them: Pierce one end with your fingernail and then slip the bean out of its skin.

Chapter 7

satisfying sides

satisfying sides

persian-spiced quinoa

SERVES 6

1 ½ teaspoons unsalted butter

▲ **1 small onion, diced**

▲ **1 cup quinoa, rinsed and drained**

1 cinnamon stick

4 whole cardamom pods

1 ½ cups water

Pinch saffron threads or ground turmeric

¾ teaspoon salt

¼ cup dried currants or chopped black raisins

3 tablespoons toasted sliced almonds

1 Melt butter in medium saucepan over medium heat. Add onion and cook, stirring frequently, until softened, about 3 minutes. Stir in quinoa, cinnamon stick, and cardamom; cook, stirring constantly, 1 minute. Add water, saffron, and salt; bring to boil. Stir once, reduce heat, and cover pan. Simmer until water is absorbed and quinoa is translucent and tender, about 15 minutes.

2 Remove quinoa from heat and let stand, covered, 5 minutes. Remove cinnamon stick and cardamom pods. Add currants and almonds, and fluff with fork.

Per serving (generous ½ cup): 151 Cal, 4 g Total Fat, 1 g Sat Fat, 0 g Trans Fat, 3 mg Chol, 295 mg Sod, 24 g Carb, 5 g Sugar, 3 g Fib, 5 g Prot, 33 mg Calc.

For Your Information

You may substitute ½ teaspoon ground cardamom for the cardamom pods, if you like.

wild rice and apple pilaf

SERVES 6

- ▲ **1 cup wild and brown rice blend**
- ▲ **1 small onion, diced**
- ▲ **1 cup reduced-sodium vegetable or chicken broth**
- **1 cup apple cider**
- **1 bay leaf**
- **¼ teaspoon salt**
- ▲ **1 apple, peeled, cored, and chopped**
- **¼ cup pecan halves, chopped**

1 In medium saucepan, combine rice, onion, broth, cider, bay leaf, and salt. Bring to boil. Stir once, reduce heat, and cover. Simmer 40 minutes.

2 Sprinkle apple over rice. Cover pan and continue to simmer until liquid is absorbed, about 5 minutes more. Remove from heat and let stand, covered, 10 minutes. Remove and discard bay leaf. Sprinkle rice with pecans and fluff with fork.

Per serving (⅔ cup): 200 Cal, 4 g Total Fat, 1 g Sat Fat, 0 g Trans Fat, 0 mg Chol, 128 mg Sod, 38 g Carb, 9 g Sugar, 3 g Fib, 3 g Prot, 11 mg Calc.

Stay On Track

For more crunch and fiber, double the amount of apple in this recipe and garnish the finished dish with 3 thinly sliced scallions.

WILD RICE AND APPLE PILAF

savory lemon-parsley millet

1 ½ teaspoons unsalted butter

1 garlic clove, minced

▲ 1 cup millet

2 cups water

½ teaspoon salt

Zest and juice of 1 lemon

▲ 1 bunch scallions, thinly sliced

3 tablespoons chopped fresh parsley

1 Melt butter in medium saucepan over medium heat. Add garlic and cook, stirring, until fragrant, about 1 minute. Stir in millet and cook 1 minute. Add water and salt; bring to boil. Reduce heat, cover, and simmer until liquid is absorbed, about 20 minutes.

2 Stir in lemon zest and juice. Remove pan from heat and let stand, covered, 10 minutes. Add scallions and parsley, and fluff with fork.

Per serving (generous ½ cup): 148 Cal, 2 g Total Fat, 1 g Sat Fat, 0 g Trans Fat, 3 mg Chol, 205 mg Sod, 28 g Carb, 1 g Sugar, 4 g Fib, 4 g Prot, 34 mg Calc.

For Your Information

Trying to eat more whole grains? Then you should definitely give millet a try. This tiny yellow grain has a mild nutty flavor and cooks up quickly. Look for it in natural foods stores. This full-flavored treatment is superb with fish or poultry.

quick polenta with spinach

SERVES 4

1 ½ cups + 1 tablespoon water

¼ teaspoon salt

▲ **½ cup instant polenta**

▲ **4 cups (2 ½ ounces) baby spinach, coarsely chopped**

2 tablespoons grated Parmesan cheese

1 Bring water and salt to boil in medium saucepan over medium-high heat. Slowly whisk in polenta. Using a spoon, stir in spinach. Reduce heat to medium-low and cook, stirring, until polenta is very thick, about 4 minutes.

2 Remove polenta from heat and stir in Parmesan. Serve immediately, or pour polenta into nonstick pie pan, let cool, and cut into 8 wedges.

Per serving (½ cup or 2 wedges): 107 Cal, 2 g Total Fat, 1 g Sat Fat, 0 g Trans Fat, 4 mg Chol, 409 mg Sod, 18 g Carb, 1 g Sugar, 2 g Fib, 4 g Prot, 81 mg Calc.

Make Ahead

Cooled polenta will keep covered with plastic wrap and refrigerated up to 4 days. To reheat, place it on a baking sheet sprayed with nonstick spray and broil until heated through, about 4 minutes.

**KASHA WITH
SUMMER SQUASH**

kasha with summer squash

SERVES 6

2 teaspoons olive oil

▲ 1 small red onion, chopped

▲ 1 medium zucchini, chopped

▲ 1 small yellow squash, chopped

▲ 1 red bell pepper, chopped

▲ 2 cups reduced-sodium vegetable broth

▲ 1 cup kasha

▲ 1 large egg, lightly beaten

½ teaspoon salt

2 tablespoons chopped fresh parsley

1 Heat 1 teaspoon oil in large nonstick skillet over medium-high heat. Add onion, zucchini, yellow squash, and bell pepper. Cook, stirring occasionally, until vegetables are tender and lightly browned, about 5 minutes. Transfer vegetable mixture to plate.

2 Meanwhile, bring broth to simmer in small saucepan.

3 Combine kasha and egg in medium bowl and mix to combine. Heat remaining 1 teaspoon oil in same skillet over medium-high heat. Add kasha mixture and cook, stirring, until grains separate, about 1 minute. Stir in simmering broth and salt. Reduce heat and simmer, covered, until liquid has been absorbed and kasha is tender, 8–10 minutes. Add vegetable mixture and cook, stirring occasionally, until heated through, about 1 minute. Stir in parsley.

Per serving (1 cup): 144 Cal, 3 g Total Fat, 1 g Sat Fat, 0 g Trans Fat, 36 mg Chol, 260 mg Sod, 26 g Carb, 3 g Sugar, 4 g Fib, 5 g Prot, 28 mg Calc.

For Your Information

Kasha is made from roasted hulled grains of buckwheat and has a wonderfully rich and nutty flavor. It is traditionally coated with egg before cooking to keep the grains separate and prevent it from becoming mushy.

risotto-style slow-cooker barley and peas

SERVES 6

- ▲ 2 ¾ cups low-sodium chicken or vegetable broth
- ▲ 1 cup pearl barley, rinsed
- ½ cup dry white wine
- 2 shallots, finely chopped
- ¼ teaspoon salt
- ▲ 1 cup frozen peas
- ¼ cup grated Parmesan cheese
- Black pepper to taste

Combine broth, barley, wine, shallots, and salt in slow cooker. Cover and cook on low until barley is tender and liquid is almost completely absorbed, 4 ½–5 hours. Add peas and cook 20 minutes more. Stir in Parmesan. Serve each portion sprinkled with lots of black pepper.

Per serving (¾ cup): 180 Cal, 2 g Total Fat, 1 g Sat Fat, 0 g Trans Fat, 3 mg Chol, 197 mg Sod, 31 g Carb, 2 g Sugar, 6 g Fib, 7 g Prot, 56 mg Calc.

Stay On Track
If you'd like more veggies in your risotto, add 1 or 2 diced carrots and 1 or 2 diced celery stalks to the slow cooker along with the shallots.

farro with white beans

SERVES 6

- 1 cup farro
- 1 tablespoon grated lemon zest
- 2 tablespoons lemon juice
- 2 teaspoons olive oil
- 1 teaspoon Dijon mustard
- ¼ teaspoon salt
- ¼ teaspoon black pepper
- 1 cup canned no-salt-added white beans, rinsed and drained
- 8 kalamata olives, pitted and coarsely chopped
- 2 tablespoons chopped fresh parsley

1 Prepare farro according to package directions, omitting salt.

2 To make dressing, whisk together lemon zest and juice, oil, mustard, salt, and pepper in large bowl. Add farro, beans, olives, and parsley; toss to combine. Serve warm or at room temperature.

Per serving (¾ cup): 171 Cal, 3 g Total Fat, 0 g Sat Fat, 0 g Trans Fat, 0 mg Chol, 233 mg Sod, 29 g Carb, 1 g Sugar, 4 g Fib, 7 g Prot, 45 mg Calc.

For Your Information

Farro is a species of wheat similar to spelt and wheat berries. The good news is that it cooks up quite quickly—in about 25 minutes. Look for farro in Italian specialty markets or natural foods stores.

crispy hasselback yukon potatoes

SERVES 4

- **4 medium (5-ounce) Yukon Gold potatoes, scrubbed**
- **2 teaspoons olive oil**
- **1 garlic clove, minced**
- **½ teaspoon salt**
- **¼ teaspoon black pepper**

1 Preheat oven to 425°F. Line small baking sheet with parchment paper. Set aside.

2 Peel potatoes, leaving a strip of skin on one long side of each for potato to rest on. Lay, skin side down, on cutting board and slice each into ⅙-inch slices, cutting only two-thirds of the way through.

3 Drizzle each potato with ½ teaspoon oil and gently spread slices to let oil get in-between. Sprinkle potatoes with garlic, salt, and pepper, again spreading open slices to get seasoning in-between. Place on prepared baking sheet and bake until potatoes are browned and crisp, about 50 minutes.

Per serving (1 potato): 117 Cal, 2 g Total Fat, 0 g Sat Fat, 0 g Trans Fat, 0 mg Chol, 291 mg Sod, 26 g Carb, 3 g Sugar, 3 g Fib, 4 g Prot, 21 mg Calc.

For Your Information

These unique baked potatoes are named after Stockholm's historic Hasselbacken Hotel, and are sometimes known as accordion potatoes. For foolproof slicing, place each potato lengthwise between two wooden chopsticks to prevent your knife from cutting all the way through the potato.

roast golden beets with hazelnuts
SERVES 4

- 1 ½ **pounds golden baby beets with tops**
- 2 **teaspoons olive oil**
- 3 **garlic cloves, thinly sliced**
- 2 **shallots, thinly sliced**
- ¼ **teaspoon salt**
- 2 **tablespoons chopped hazelnuts, toasted**

1 Preheat oven to 400°F. Trim beets; reserve tops. Place beet roots on center of double layer of foil and fold edges together to seal tightly. Place packet on baking sheet and roast until beets are fork-tender, about 45 minutes. Unwrap beets and let cool. Peel and cut beets in half.

2 Rinse beet greens well and coarsely chop. Heat oil in large nonstick skillet over medium heat. Add garlic and cook, stirring occasionally, until golden, 1–2 minutes. Add beet greens, shallots, and salt. Cook, partially covered, until greens are tender, 8–10 minutes. Add roasted beets; cook, stirring often, until heated through, about 2 minutes. Transfer to serving bowl; sprinkle with hazelnuts. Serve hot or at room temperature.

Per serving (¾ cup): 125 Cal, 5 g Total Fat, 1 g Sat Fat, 0 g Trans Fat, 0 mg Chol, 281 mg Sod, 19 g Carb, 12 g Sugar, 5 g Fib, 4 g Prot, 46 mg Calc.

For Your Information
Golden beets are a joy to work with; they lack the deep-purple pigment red beets have, so your hands and cutting board won't be stained. To peel roast beets, simply rub them with a paper towel; the skin should fall away easily.

caramelized root vegetables with balsami

▲ **3 parsnips (¾ pound), peeled, halved lengthwise through thickest parts, and cut into 1-inch pieces**

3 garlic cloves, finely chopped

1 ½ teaspoons olive oil

¾ teaspoon salt

▲ **2 turnips (¾ pound), peeled and cut into ¾-inch chunks**

▲ **3 beets (1 pound), peeled and cut into ¾-inch chunks**

1 tablespoon balsamic vinegar

1 tablespoon chopped fresh chives

1 Preheat oven to 450°F. Line large rimmed baking sheet with parchment paper.

2 Place parsnips in medium bowl and toss with 1 clove garlic, ½ teaspoon olive oil, and ¼ teaspoon salt. Lay in single layer on one third of prepared baking sheet. Repeat with turnips and beets, using remaining garlic, oil, and salt and keeping vegetables separate. Roast vegetables until browned and cooked through, stirring once or twice, 35–40 minutes.

3 Transfer vegetables to bowl. Drizzle with vinegar and sprinkle with chives.

Per serving (¾ cup): 86 Cal, 1 g Total Fat, 0 g Sat Fat, 0 g Trans Fat, 0 mg Chol, 356 mg Sod, 18 g Carb, 7 g Sugar, 5 g Fib, 2 g Prot, 43 mg Calc.

For Your Information
This recipe calls for keeping the vegetables separate while they roast to prevent the beets from staining the parsnips and turnips red. If you use golden beets, staining is not an issue and you can omit this step.

CARAMELIZED
ROOT VEGETABLES
WITH BALSAMIC

MANAGING PORTION SIZE

It's not only *what* we eat, but also *how much* we eat that affects our weight-loss results. But the amount of foods we put on our plates is influenced by many factors, some of which make it difficult to stick to an eating plan. The good news is that there are lots of tried-and-true strategies for taking control.

Keep a stash of snack-size baggies on hand. Once you're home from the grocery store, spend a few minutes transferring individual servings of cereal, crackers, and other foods to small zip-close bags. Label each with the *PointsPlus* value for easy tracking.

Use smaller plates. Studies show that the size of the plate from which we eat can affect how much we eat and what we perceive a satisfying portion to be. Try using plates that are no more than 8 to 10 inches in diameter.

Don't place serving dishes on the table. You'll be more tempted to take seconds if food is too conveniently placed.

Avoid multitasking during meals. Distractions like TV, computers, or talking on the phone can cause you to eat too quickly, making it difficult to pay attention to your body's satiety signals. Commit to eating sitting down and focusing only on your food (or dining partners), and you'll be more likely to stick to your meal plan.

Share an entrée when you dine out. Restaurant portions are typically quite large, so splitting a single order with a friend is often a healthy (and economical) option. Alternatively, you can ask your waiter to serve you only half the portion and pack the other half in a doggie bag that you can take home.

End your meal with a piece of fruit. Consider doing this even if you intend to have a dessert later. It will help fill you up and take the edge off your sweet tooth, both things that will make a right-size dessert more likely to satisfy.

Get leftovers stored quickly. Don't leave foods out where they might tempt you to overeat. Refrigerate what you intend to eat in the next few days and freeze the rest.

creamed kale with raisins
SERVES 4

- ½ **onion, diced**
- ¼ **cup golden raisins**
- ⅓ **cup water**
- ¼ **teaspoon salt**
- 1 (¾-**pound) bunch green curly kale, stems and tough ribs discarded, leaves thinly sliced**
- ¼ **cup light cream cheese (Neufchâtel)**
- 3 **tablespoons fat-free half-and-half**
- ¼ **teaspoon black pepper**
- **Large pinch ground nutmeg**

1 Place onion, raisins, water, salt, and half of kale in large saucepan and set over medium heat. Cover and cook until kale is wilted, about 2 minutes. Stir in remaining kale. Reduce heat to medium-low; cover and cook, stirring occasionally, until kale is very tender, 15–20 minutes.

2 Stir in cream cheese, half-and-half, pepper, and nutmeg. Stir until cream cheese is melted and ingredients are combined.

Per serving (½ cup): 119 Cal, 3 g Total Fat, 1 g Sat Fat, 0 g Trans Fat, 8 mg Chol, 266 mg Sod, 20 g Carb, 10 g Sugar, 3 g Fib, 5 g Prot, 163 mg Calc.

Make Ahead
This creamed kale will keep up to 4 days in the refrigerator. To reheat, transfer it to a microwavable bowl and cook, stirring once or twice, until hot, 2 to 3 minutes. You can also reheat it in a small saucepan on the stovetop.

stewed greens with bacon

SERVES 6

3 slices turkey bacon, chopped

▲ **1 (¾-pound) bunch Swiss chard, stems removed, leaves sliced**

▲ **1 (¾-pound) bunch mustard greens, stems removed, leaves sliced**

▲ **4 scallions, finely chopped**

¼ cup water

2 teaspoons sherry vinegar

¼ teaspoon salt

Pinch red pepper flakes

1 Cook bacon in large nonstick skillet over medium heat, stirring occasionally, until browned, about 5 minutes. With slotted spoon, transfer to plate lined with paper towels.

2 Add Swiss chard to skillet; cook, stirring, until wilted, about 2 minutes. Add mustard greens, scallions, water, vinegar, salt, and pepper flakes. Cover and cook, stirring occasionally, until greens are very tender, 10–15 minutes.

3 Uncover skillet; continue to cook until most of liquid has evaporated. Stir in bacon.

Per serving (¾ cup): 56 Cal, 2 g Total Fat, 1 g Sat Fat, 0 g Trans Fat, 7 mg Chol, 395 mg Sod, 6 g Carb, 2 g Sugar, 3 g Fib, 5 g Prot, 96 mg Calc.

For Your Information
This is a traditional way to cook hearty greens and will work with almost any variety, such as collards, kale, beet greens, or turnip greens.

steamed green beans with carrot-ginger sauce

SERVES 6

- **2 carrots, thinly sliced**
- **⅓ cup reduced-sodium vegetable broth**
- **1 tablespoon lemon juice**
- **1 ¼ teaspoons grated peeled fresh ginger**
- **¾ teaspoon sugar**
- **½ teaspoon salt**
- **1 pound green beans, trimmed**

1 Put carrots in steamer basket; set in large saucepan over 1 inch of boiling water. Cover tightly and steam until very tender, about 8 minutes. Transfer carrots to food processor (leave steamer basket and water in pot). Add broth, lemon juice, ginger, sugar, and salt to carrots; puree.

2 Place green beans in steamer basket and steam until beans are crisp tender, about 6 minutes. Serve drizzled with sauce.

Per serving (¾ cup beans and 2 tablespoons sauce):
35 Cal, 0 g Total Fat, 0 g Sat Fat, 0 g Trans Fat, 0 mg Chol, 220 mg Sod, 8 g Carb, 3 g Sugar, 3 g Fib, 2 g Prot, 36 mg Calc.

Make Ahead

This colorful side is delicious at room temperature and can be made up to 3 days ahead: Prepare the dressing, cover, and refrigerate. Steam the green beans and cool under cold running water. Wrap them in paper towels, and place them in a plastic bag. Dress the beans just before serving.

baked squash with pancetta and pine nuts

SERVES 4

- **2 small delicata or acorn squash, halved, seeds scraped out**
- **1 teaspoon olive oil**
- **1 teaspoon maple syrup**
- **¼ teaspoon salt**
- **2 (½-ounce) slices pancetta, diced**
- **2 tablespoons pine nuts, chopped**
- **10 fresh sage leaves, thinly sliced**

1 Preheat oven to 400°F. Brush squash halves all over with oil. Brush insides (not skin side) with maple syrup and sprinkle with salt. Place, skin side down, on baking sheet and bake until very tender, about 45 minutes.

2 Meanwhile, place pancetta in small skillet and set over medium heat. Cook, stirring frequently, until pancetta is browned and crisped, about 5 minutes. Stir in pine nuts and sage, and cook 2 minutes more.

3 When squash is very tender, sprinkle insides with pancetta mixture and bake 5 minutes more.

Per serving (1 squash half and 1 generous tablespoon **topping):** 144 Cal, 5 g Total Fat, 1 g Sat Fat, 0 g Trans Fat, 6 mg Chol, 343 mg Sod, 24 g Carb, 6 g Sugar, 3 g Fib, 4 g Prot, 73 mg Calc.

For Your Information

Delicata is one of the tastiest small winter squashes available, with creamy, sweet flesh and a festively striped exterior. Acorn, dumpling, or carnival squash will also work excellently in this recipe.

roasted cauliflower with lemon and cumin

SERVES 4

- **1 small head cauliflower, cut into small florets**
- **2 teaspoons canola oil**
- **½ teaspoon ground cumin**
- **¼ teaspoon salt**
- **Zest and juice of ½ lemon**
- **1 garlic clove, minced**

1 Preheat oven to 450°F.

2 Place cauliflower on large rimmed baking sheet. Drizzle with oil and sprinkle with cumin and salt. Toss to coat. Spread cauliflower in single layer on baking sheet. Roast, stirring once, 15 minutes. Sprinkle cauliflower with lemon zest and juice and garlic; toss to coat. Roast until cauliflower is just tender, about 5 minutes longer.

Per serving (1 cup): 42 Cal, 2 g Total Fat, 0 g Sat Fat, 0 g Trans Fat, 0 mg Chol, 166 mg Sod, 5 g Carb, 2 g Sugar, 2 g Fib, 1 g Prot, 21 mg Calc.

Stay On Track

Adding 1 red or yellow bell pepper along with the cauliflower in step 2 will increase the color, flavor, and nutrients of this dish and give you bigger portions without increasing the *PointsPlus* value.

ROASTED GARLIC AND
HERB BREAD

roasted garlic and herb bread

SERVES 6

1 garlic bulb

2 tablespoons grated Parmesan cheese

½ teaspoon Italian seasoning

½ (12-ounce) whole grain baguette, halved lengthwise

1 Preheat oven to 375°F. Cut garlic head crosswise in half to expose cloves. Lightly spray garlic all over with nonstick spray and wrap in foil. Place on oven rack and roast until garlic cloves are browned and meltingly tender, about 1 hour. Let cool.

2 When cool enough to handle, unwrap garlic and use a knife to remove soft pulp from white husk. Place garlic in bowl; add Parmesan and seasoning blend. Mash with fork until smooth.

3 Preheat broiler. Spread garlic mixture over cut sides of baguette. Broil 6 inches from heat until browned, about 2 minutes. Cut into 12 pieces and serve at once.

Per serving (2 pieces garlic bread): 93 Cal, 1 g Total Fat, 0 g Sat Fat, 0 g Trans Fat, 1 mg Chol, 182 mg Sod, 17 g Carb, 1 g Sugar, 2 g Fib, 4 g Prot, 31 mg Calc.

For Your Information

For anyone who's not fond of garlic, a spread made with roast shallots is also delicious. Simply peel and halve 2 small shallots and bake them as described in step 1.

scallion-walnut cornbread

- ¾ cup stone-ground yellow cornmeal
- ¾ cup all-purpose flour
- 1 teaspoon baking powder
- ½ teaspoon baking soda
- ¼ teaspoon salt
- ¾ cup low-fat buttermilk
- ½ cup unsweetened applesauce
- 1 large egg
- 2 tablespoons canola oil
- 1 tablespoon honey
- 4 scallions, thinly sliced
- ⅓ cup chopped walnuts

1 Preheat oven to 400°F. Spray 8-inch square baking pan with nonstick spray. Line bottom with wax paper and spray paper.

2 Whisk cornmeal, flour, baking powder, baking soda, and salt together in medium bowl. Whisk buttermilk, applesauce, egg, oil, and honey together in another bowl. Pour buttermilk mixture into cornmeal mixture and stir until combined. Fold in scallions and walnuts.

3 Scrape batter into prepared baking pan and smooth top to level. Bake until toothpick inserted into center comes out clean, about 30 minutes. Cool 10 minutes; then cut into 9 squares.

Per serving (1 square): 175 Cal, 7 g Total Fat, 1 g Sat Fat, 0 g Trans Fat, 25 mg Chol, 226 mg Sod, 25 g Carb, 4 g Sugar, 1 g Fib, 4 g Prot, 48 mg Calc.

Make Ahead

To store and serve later, let the cornbread cool completely on a wire rack. Place the squares in a zip-close plastic bag; they'll keep up to 2 days at room temperature. Or place the bag in the freezer and freeze up to 3 months. To reheat, thaw the bread overnight in the refrigerator if frozen.

braised red cabbage and pears

SERVES 6

- ▲ **1 small (1 ⅓-pound) head red cabbage, quartered**
- ▲ **1 small onion, halved and thinly sliced**
- ▲ **2 pears, cored and sliced**
- **2 tablespoons cider vinegar**
- **2 tablespoons pear juice, apple juice, or water**
- **¾ teaspoon salt**
- **¼ teaspoon black pepper**
- **2 tablespoons chopped fresh parsley**

1 Cut out and discard solid white core from each cabbage quarter. Thinly slice cabbage and transfer to large saucepan. Add onion, pears, vinegar, pear juice, salt, and pepper. Cook, covered, over medium heat until cabbage wilts, about 10 minutes.

2 Reduce heat to medium-low and cook, stirring occasionally, until cabbage is very tender, about 30 minutes (add a tablespoon or two of water if the cabbage begins to dry out). Stir in parsley.

Per serving (¾ cup): 74 Cal, 0 g Total Fat, 0 g Sat Fat, 0 g Trans Fat, 0 mg Chol, 318 mg Sod, 19 g Carb, 10 g Sugar, 4 g Fib, 2 g Prot, 53 mg Calc.

Chapter 8

home-style desserts

home-style desserts

almond torte with mixed berries
SERVES 10

- **1 cup all-purpose flour**
- **1 teaspoon baking powder**
- **¼ teaspoon salt**
- ▲ **¼ cup fat-free milk**
- **1 teaspoon vanilla extract**
- **⅓ cup almond paste**
- **⅓ cup sugar**
- **¼ cup unsalted butter, at room temperature**
- ▲ **½ cup fat-free egg substitute, at room temperature**
- ▲ **3 ⅓ cups mixed berries**

1 Preheat oven to 350°F. Spray 8-inch round cake pan with nonstick spray. Line bottom with wax paper. Spray paper with nonstick spray; then dust with flour.

2 Whisk together flour, baking powder, and salt in small bowl. Combine milk and vanilla in small glass measure.

3 With electric mixer on medium-high speed, beat almond paste, sugar, and butter in large bowl until light and fluffy, about 5 minutes. Beat in egg substitute in two additions, beating well after each. With mixer on low speed, alternately add flour mixture and milk mixture, beginning and ending with flour mixture.

4 Scrape batter into prepared pan and spread evenly. Bake until toothpick inserted in center comes out clean, 30–35 minutes. Let cake cool in pan on wire rack 15 minutes. Remove from pan and cool completely on rack.

5 Cut cake into 10 wedges and serve with berries.

Per serving (1 wedge and ⅓ cup berries): 163 Cal, 7 g Total Fat, 3 g Sat Fat, 0 g Trans Fat, 12 mg Chol, 136 mg Sod, 23 g Carb, 2 g Fib, 11 g Sugar, 4 g Prot, 47 mg Calc.

Make Ahead
If you like, tightly wrap the cooled cake in plastic wrap and then in heavy-duty foil, and freeze up to 3 months. To serve, thaw at room temperature overnight and proceed with step 5.

pecan praline cheesecake

SERVES 20

CRUST

¾ cup chopped pecans

½ cup all-purpose flour

1 tablespoon sugar

3 tablespoons unsalted butter, melted

FILLING AND TOPPING

3 (8-ounce) packages fat-free cream cheese, at room temperature

1 (14-ounce) can fat-free sweetened condensed milk

¾ teaspoon vanilla extract

¼ teaspoon almond extract

Pinch salt

▲ **¾ cup fat-free egg substitute, at room temperature**

½ cup fat-free caramel topping

¼ cup coarsely chopped pecans

1 Preheat oven to 350°F. Spray 9-inch springform pan with nonstick spray.

2 To make crust, pulse pecans, flour, and sugar in food processor until pecans are finely ground. Add butter and pulse until combined. Press crust evenly over bottom of prepared pan. Bake until golden brown, about 15 minutes. Cool crust completely on rack. Reduce oven temperature to 300°F.

3 To make filling, with electric mixer on medium speed, beat cream cheese in large bowl until fluffy. Gradually beat in milk, vanilla, almond extract, and salt. Beat in egg substitute in three additions, beating well after each. Scrape batter into prepared pan and spread evenly. Bake until side is puffed and center still jiggles slightly, 60–65 minutes. Cool cake completely on rack. Refrigerate, covered, until thoroughly chilled, at least 8 hours or up to 2 days.

4 To serve, run knife around inside edge of pan; release and remove side. Stir caramel topping and pecans together in small bowl; drizzle over top of cake. Cut cake into 20 wedges with serrated knife dipped into hot water and wiped dry after each cut.

Per serving (1 wedge): 183 Cal, 6 g Total Fat, 2 g Sat Fat, 0 g Trans Fat, 11 mg Chol, 305 mg Sod, 24 g Carb, 1 g Fib, 8 g Prot, 182 mg Calc.

PECAN PRALINE
CHEESECAKE

rich chocolate-beet cake squares

SERVES 12

- ¾ cup whole wheat pastry flour
- ½ cup all-purpose flour
- ¾ cup granulated sugar
- ¼ cup unsweetened cocoa
- ½ teaspoon baking soda
- ¼ teaspoon salt
- ½ cup low-fat buttermilk
- ¼ cup fat-free milk
- 2 tablespoons canola oil
- 2 large eggs
- 1 teaspoon vanilla extract
- 1 ½ cups shredded peeled cooked beets
- 1 teaspoon confectioners' sugar

1 Preheat oven to 350°F. Spray 8-inch square baking pan with nonstick spray; then dust with flour.

2 Whisk together whole wheat flour, all-purpose flour, granulated sugar, cocoa, baking soda, and salt in medium bowl. Whisk together buttermilk, milk, oil, eggs, and vanilla in large bowl. Stir in beets. Add flour mixture to beet mixture and stir just until combined.

3 Pour batter into prepared baking pan. Bake until toothpick inserted into center comes out clean, 30–35 minutes. Let cake cool in pan on wire rack 15 minutes. Remove from pan and let cool on rack. Sprinkle cake with confectioners' sugar; cut into 12 squares.

Per serving (1 square): 128 Cal, 4 g Total Fat, 1 g Sat Fat, 0 g Trans Fat, 36 mg Chol, 138 mg Sod, 23 g Carb, 11 g Sugar, 2 g Fib, 3 g Prot, 32 mg Calc.

For Your Information

Beets make this cake supermoist and intensify the flavor of the cocoa. You can buy precooked beets or individually wrap raw unpeeled beets in foil and roast them in a 375°F oven until tender, about 1 hour. Cool and rub with a paper towel to remove skins.

chocolate cupcakes with coconut-pecan frosting

SERVES 12

5 tablespoons sweetened flaked coconut

3 tablespoons chopped pecans

½ cup well-shaken fat-free evaporated milk

1 tablespoon cornstarch

3 tablespoons packed light brown sugar

1 tablespoon unsalted butter, melted

2 ounces sweetened baking chocolate, finely chopped

¼ cup boiling water

½ cup plain low-fat yogurt

3 tablespoons canola oil

2 large egg whites

1 ⅔ cups all-purpose flour

1 cup granulated sugar

1 teaspoon baking soda

½ teaspoon salt

1 Preheat oven to 350°F. Line 12-cup muffin pan with paper liners.

2 To make frosting, toast coconut and pecans on large rimmed baking sheet, stirring once, until lightly browned, 8–10 minutes; let cool. Meanwhile, whisk together milk and cornstarch in small heavy saucepan. Set saucepan over medium-high heat, and cook, whisking constantly, until thickened, 2–3 minutes. Remove from heat. Add brown sugar and butter, and whisk until sugar has dissolved. Transfer to medium bowl and let cool to room temperature. Cover and refrigerate until chilled, about 1 hour.

3 Meanwhile, to make cupcakes, place chocolate in medium bowl, add boiling water, and whisk until smooth. Whisk in yogurt and oil. Whisk in egg whites. Whisk together flour, granulated sugar, baking soda, and salt in large bowl. Pour chocolate mixture into flour mixture and whisk just until combined. Spoon batter evenly into prepared muffin cups. Bake until toothpick inserted in centers of cupcakes comes out clean, about 30 minutes. Cool in pan on rack 10 minutes. Turn cupcakes out of pan and cool completely on rack.

4 Just before serving, stir coconut and pecans into frosting mixture. Spread frosting on top of each cupcake.

Per serving (1 frosted cupcake): 218 Cal, 8 g Total Fat, 3 g Sat Fat, 0 g Trans Fat, 3 mg Chol, 239 mg Sod, 36 g Carb, 21 g Sugar, 1 g Fib, 4 g Prot, 59 mg Calc.

lemon-poppy seed cupcakes
SERVES 12

1 ⅔ cups all-purpose flour

2 tablespoons poppy seeds

2 teaspoons baking powder

¼ teaspoon salt

1 ¼ cups sugar

⅓ cup canola oil

1 tablespoon finely grated lemon zest

▲ ½ cup fat-free egg substitute

▲ ½ cup fat-free milk

¼ cup fresh lemon juice

12 very thin slices from small lemon, seeds removed

1 Preheat oven to 350°F. Line 12-cup muffin pan with paper liners.

2 Whisk together flour, poppy seeds, baking powder, and salt in medium bowl. With electric mixer on medium speed, beat ¾ cup sugar, oil, and lemon zest in large bowl until combined. Beat in egg substitute in two additions, beating well after each. Beat in milk. Reduce speed to low and beat in flour mixture.

3 Spoon batter evenly into prepared muffin cups. Bake until toothpick inserted into centers of cupcakes comes out clean, 22–24 minutes. Cool cupcakes in pan on rack 10 minutes.

4 Meanwhile, combine remaining ½ cup sugar and lemon juice in small saucepan and set over medium-high heat. Cook, stirring, until sugar has dissolved. Add lemon slices and cook, stirring, 2 minutes. Remove pan from heat. With fork, pick up slices, shaking excess liquid back into pan, and place slices in bowl. Bring liquid to boil; cook, stirring frequently, until syrup has thickened slightly, 3–4 minutes. Remove cupcakes from pan and place on rack. Put wax paper under rack to catch drips.

5 Remove paper liners from cupcakes. With toothpick, prick cupcakes all over about 1-inch deep. Brush syrup on top and side of cupcakes; if glaze does not sink into cupcakes, prick again. Arrange 1 lemon slice on top of each cupcake. Cool completely on rack. Store in airtight container.

Per serving (1 glazed cupcake): 188 Cal, 7 g Total Fat, 1 g Sat Fat, 0 g Trans Fat, 0 mg Chol, 160 mg Sod, 30 g Carb, 16 g Sugar, 1 g Fib, 3 g Prot, 58 mg Calc.

rosemary apple tart

SERVES 6

1 sheet frozen puff pastry (from 17.3-ounce package), thawed

6 tablespoons sugar

1 teaspoon all-purpose flour

2 tablespoons chopped walnuts

1 teaspoon grated lemon zest

1 teaspoon chopped fresh rosemary

4 apples, peeled, halved, cored, and cut crosswise into ¼-inch-thick slices

1 Preheat oven to 400°F. Line large baking sheet with parchment paper.

2 Unfold puff pastry onto lightly floured surface. With floured rolling pin, roll pastry to 10 x 14-inch rectangle. Place on prepared baking sheet and refrigerate 10 minutes.

3 Stir together 1 tablespoon sugar and flour in small bowl. Stir together remaining 5 tablespoons sugar, walnuts, lemon zest, and rosemary in another bowl. Sprinkle flour mixture over pastry, leaving ½-inch border around edge. Starting at short side, arrange apple slices on pastry in three rows, overlapping slices. Sprinkle apples with sugar-and-walnut mixture.

4 Bake until pastry has browned and apples are tender, about 40 minutes. With spatula, loosen tart from parchment and slide onto wire rack to cool. Cut into 6 pieces.

Per serving (⅙ of tart): 128 Cal, 4 g Total Fat, 1 g Sat Fat, 0 g Trans Fat, 0 mg Chol, 33 mg Sod, 26 g Carb, 20 g Sugar, 2 g Fib, 1 g Prot, 9 mg Calc.

For Your Information
For best results choose a good baking apple like Golden Delicious or Gala for this superb tart.

molasses pumpkin pie

SERVES 12

CRUST

- **1 ¼ cups all-purpose flour**
- **1 tablespoon confectioners' sugar**
- **½ teaspoon salt**
- **3 tablespoons canola oil**
- **2 tablespoons cold unsalted butter, cut into small pieces**
- **3–4 tablespoons ice-cold water**
- **1 teaspoon cider vinegar**

FILLING

- ▲ **1 (15-ounce) can pumpkin puree**
- **1 cup well-shaken fat-free evaporated milk**
- **¾ cup packed brown sugar**
- ▲ **½ cup fat-free egg substitute**
- **1 tablespoon molasses**
- **1 teaspoon vanilla extract**
- **¾ teaspoon pumpkin pie spice**
- **Pinch salt**

1 To make crust, pulse flour, confectioners' sugar, and salt in food processor until combined. Add oil and butter; pulse until mixture resembles coarse crumbs. Combine water and vinegar in glass measure; slowly pour through feed tube, pulsing just until dough begins to form. Shape dough into disk. Wrap in plastic wrap and refrigerate at least 30 minutes or up to 1 day.

2 Position rack in middle of oven; preheat oven to 425°F.

3 Roll out dough on lightly floured work surface to 12-inch round. Transfer dough to 9-inch pie plate and gently press pastry against side and bottom of pie plate. Turn edge under and crimp. With fork, prick bottom and side of crust all over. Bake until edge is just beginning to brown, 12–15 minutes. Cool on rack.

4 Position rack on lowest shelf of oven and reduce oven temperature to 350°F. To make filling, whisk all filling ingredients together in large bowl, whisking until smooth. Scrape into crust and spread evenly. Bake until center is firm, about 65 minutes. Cool completely on rack. Cut into 12 wedges.

Per serving (1 wedge): 185 Cal, 6 g Total Fat, 2 g Sat Fat, 0 g Trans Fat, 6 mg Chol, 140 mg Sod, 31 g Carb, 19 g Sugar, 1 g Fib, 3 g Prot, 89 mg Calc.

cherry-berry cobbler with sour cream biscuits

SERVES 9

- ▲ **3 cups pitted cherries**
- ▲ **2 pints blueberries**
- **½ cup packed light brown sugar**
- **2 tablespoons water**
- **4 teaspoons cornstarch**
- **1 tablespoon fresh lemon juice**
- **1 ½ cups self-rising flour (not cake flour)**
- **¼ teaspoon salt**
- ▲ **1 ½ cups fat-free sour cream**
- **1 tablespoon turbinado sugar**

1 Position rack in lower third of oven; preheat oven to 450°F.

2 To make filling, combine cherries, blueberries, brown sugar, water, cornstarch, and lemon juice in large saucepan. Set over medium-high heat and bring to boil, stirring constantly. Reduce heat and simmer, stirring frequently, until fruit is softened and mixture is thick, about 4 minutes. Scrape mixture into 8-inch square baking dish and spread evenly.

3 To make biscuits, stir together flour and salt in medium bowl. With a rubber spatula, stir in sour cream just until dough begins to form. On well-floured surface, knead dough several times with floured hands. Pat out dough to ¾-inch thick. With floured 2-inch round cutter, cut out biscuits; gently gather scraps and pat out again to make total of 9 biscuits. Sprinkle tops with turbinado sugar and transfer to baking dish. Bake until fruit is bubbling and biscuits are browned, 20–25 minutes. Cool 15 minutes; serve warm.

Per serving (about ¾ cup fruit and 1 biscuit): 225 Cal, 3 g Total Fat, 2 g Sat Fat, 0 g Trans Fat, 8 mg Chol, 96 mg Sod, 44 g Carb, 3 g Fib, 2 g Prot, 27 mg Calc.

For Your Information

You can use fresh pitted cherries in this recipe or thawed frozen unsweetened cherries. Turbinado sugar is a raw sugar with large crystals and a light molasses flavor. You can substitute regular raw sugar or white granulated sugar.

lemony angel meringue

SERVES 8

- **4 large egg whites, at room temperature**
- **¼ teaspoon cream of tartar**
- **Pinch salt**
- **1 cup + 3 tablespoons sugar**
- **2 cups fat-free sour cream**
- **1 tablespoon fresh lemon juice**
- **1 teaspoon finely grated lemon zest**
- **3 cups mixed fresh berries**

1 Preheat oven to 225°F. Trace a 9-inch circle on parchment paper. Place paper on large baking sheet.

2 With electric mixer on medium speed, beat egg whites in large bowl until foamy. Increase speed to medium-high; add cream of tartar and salt, and beat just until soft peaks form when beaters are lifted. Gradually beat in 1 cup sugar, about two tablespoons at a time. Beat just until stiff peaks form.

3 Spoon meringue evenly inside circle on paper, making sides higher to form a nest. Bake until meringue is dry to touch, about 1 ¼ hours. Turn off oven and leave meringue in oven 3 hours. Peel off paper. If not serving immediately, wrap meringue securely in plastic wrap.

4 Just before serving, whisk sour cream, remaining 3 tablespoons sugar, lemon juice and zest in large bowl until combined. Spoon lemon filling into meringue shell, arrange berries on top, and cut into 8 wedges.

Per serving (1 wedge): 117 Cal, 0 g Total Fat, 0 g Sat Fat, 0 g Trans Fat, 6 mg Chol, 137 mg Sod, 28 g Carb, 16 g Sugar, 1 g Fib, 4 g Prot, 92 mg Calc.

Make Ahead

If you like, prepare the meringue through step 3, wrapping it as directed and storing it at room temperature up to 2 days.

LEMONY ANGEL
MERINGUE

old-fashioned apple-and-date crisp

SERVES 8

FILLING

▲ **5 large Rome apples, peeled, cored, and cut into ½-inch-thick slices**

6 pitted dates, thinly sliced

⅓ cup packed dark brown sugar

2 tablespoons lemon juice

¼ teaspoon salt

TOPPING

½ cup old-fashioned oats

¼ cup whole wheat pastry flour

¼ cup packed dark brown sugar

2 tablespoons unsalted butter, melted

Pinch salt

1 Preheat oven to 375°F. Spray 8-inch square baking dish with nonstick spray.

2 To make filling, combine apples, dates, brown sugar, lemon juice, and salt in large bowl. Scrape into prepared baking dish and spread evenly.

3 To make topping, stir together oats, flour, brown sugar, butter, and salt in medium bowl. Spread topping over filling.

4 Bake until filling is bubbling and topping is golden brown, about 1 hour. Serve warm.

Per serving (¾ cup): 201 Cal, 3 g Total Fat, 2 g Sat Fat, 0 g Trans Fat, 8 mg Chol, 96 mg Sod, 44 g Carb, 33 g Sugar, 3 g Fib, 2 g Prot, 27 mg Calc.

Make Ahead

If you like, assemble the crisp through step 3 up to 1 day ahead. Cover it tightly with plastic wrap and refrigerate. When ready to serve, remove the plastic wrap and bake as directed.

slow-cooker caramelized apples

SERVES 8

- **6 large Rome apples (3 ¼ pounds), peeled, quartered, and cored**
- **⅓ cup packed light brown sugar**
- **2 tablespoons fresh lemon juice**
- **Pinch salt**
- **¼ cup light sour cream**

1 Combine apples, brown sugar, lemon juice, and salt in 3- to 4-quart slow cooker. Cover and cook until apples are very soft and lightly caramelized, 4–6 hours on high or 8–10 hours on low.

2 Mash apples with large fork. Divide apples among 4 bowls and serve warm or at room temperature, topping each serving with ½ tablespoon sour cream.

Per serving (¾ cup apples and ½ tablespoon sour cream): 147 Cal, 1 g Total Fat, 1 g Sat Fat, 0 g Trans Fat, 3 mg Chol, 26 mg Sod, 35 g Carb, 28 g sugar, 4 g Fib, 1 g Prot, 34 mg Calc.

Make Ahead

The apples can be prepared through step 1, allowed to cool, then refrigerated in an airtight container for up to 1 week. Serve cold, or let come to room temperature before serving.

banana tea bread
with almonds and apricots

SERVES 16

½ cup sliced almonds

½ cup packed dark brown sugar

2 ½ cups all-purpose flour

2 teaspoons baking powder

1 teaspoon baking soda

½ teaspoon salt

¾ cup finely chopped dried apricots

▲ ¾ cup mashed ripe banana

⅔ cup low-fat buttermilk

▲ ½ cup fat-free egg substitute

3 tablespoons canola oil

2 teaspoons vanilla extract

1 Preheat oven to 350°F. Spray 5 x 9-inch loaf pan with nonstick spray.

2 Pulse almonds and brown sugar in food processor until almonds are finely ground. Whisk together flour, baking powder, baking soda, and salt in large bowl. Stir in almond mixture and apricots. Make a well in center of dry ingredients.

3 Whisk together banana, buttermilk, egg substitute, oil, and vanilla in medium bowl. Add to well in dry ingredients and stir with rubber spatula just until blended. Scrape into prepared pan and spread evenly.

4 Bake until top is golden brown and toothpick inserted in center comes out clean, about 1 hour. Cool loaf in pan on rack 10 minutes. Run knife around inside of pan to loosen bread. Turn bread out and let cool completely on rack. Cut into 16 slices.

Per serving (1 slice): 199 Cal, 4 g Total Fat, 0 g Sat Fat, 0 g Trans Fat, 0 mg Chol, 245 mg Sod, 35 g Carb, 12 g Sugar, 2 g Fib, 5 g Prot, 48 mg Calc.

Make Ahead

You can wrap individual slices of the bread in plastic wrap, then foil, and freeze up to 3 months. Thaw the slices at room temperature.

raspberry shortcakes with greek yogurt

SERVES 6

- 3 (6-ounce) packages fresh raspberries
- 2 tablespoons confectioners' sugar
- 1 cup plain fat-free Greek yogurt
- 2 tablespoons granulated sugar
- ½ teaspoon vanilla extract
- ½ cup whole wheat pastry flour
- ½ cup all-purpose flour
- 1 teaspoon minced crystallized ginger
- 1 teaspoon baking powder
- ¼ teaspoon baking soda
- ¼ teaspoon salt
- 2 tablespoons cold unsalted butter, cut into small pieces
- 6 tablespoons low-fat buttermilk

1 Position rack in lower third of oven; preheat oven to 400°F. Stir together raspberries and confectioners' sugar in medium bowl; let stand at room temperature. Stir together yogurt, granulated sugar, and vanilla in small bowl; refrigerate until ready to serve.

2 Whisk together whole wheat pastry flour, all-purpose flour, ginger, baking powder, baking soda, and salt in medium bowl. With pastry blender or two knives used scissor-fashion, cut butter into flour mixture until it resembles coarse crumbs. Stir in buttermilk in two additions, stirring with fork just until very sticky dough forms. Turn dough out onto floured surface and knead with floured hands about 6 times. Pat dough out to ¾-inch thick. With floured 2-inch round cutter, cut out rounds; gather scraps and reroll to make total of 6 biscuits.

3 Place biscuits, about 1 inch apart, on ungreased baking sheet and bake until golden brown, 12–15 minutes. Split biscuits and place bottoms on plates. Divide raspberry mixture evenly over biscuits, cover with tops, and dollop with yogurt mixture.

Per serving (½ cup raspberries, 1 biscuit, and 3 tablespoons yogurt): 204 Cal, 5 g Total Fat, 3 g Sat Fat, 0 g Trans Fat, 11 mg Chol, 273 mg Sod, 35 g Carb, 12 g Sugar, 7 g Fib, 7 g Prot, 92 mg Calc.

For Your Information

You can replace the raspberries with 3 cups of just about any fruit in season: Pitted cherries, sliced strawberries, sliced peaches or plums, or even diced pineapple will work well.

easy marmalade soufflés

2 teaspoons + 3 tablespoons sugar

¾ cup orange marmalade

1 tablespoon fresh lemon juice

1 tablespoon orange liqueur

¼ teaspoon salt

3 large egg whites, at room temperature

¼ teaspoon cream of tartar

1 Position rack in lower third of oven, making sure there is at least 6 inches of space above for soufflés to rise. Preheat oven to 425°F. Generously spray 4 (6-ounce) ramekins with nonstick spray and coat each with ½ teaspoon sugar.

2 Whisk together marmalade, lemon juice, liqueur, and salt in medium bowl. With electric mixer on medium speed, beat egg whites in large bowl until foamy. Add cream of tartar, increase speed to medium-high, and beat until whites form soft peaks when beaters are lifted. Gradually beat in remaining 3 tablespoons sugar; continue to beat just until stiff peaks form. With rubber spatula, fold egg whites, one third at a time, into marmalade mixture. Spoon mixture into ramekins, mounding as needed.

3 Transfer ramekins to baking sheet. Bake until soufflés are puffed and golden brown, 12–15 minutes. Serve immediately.

Per serving (1 soufflé): 189 Cal, 0 g Total Fat, 0 g Sat Fat, 0 g Trans Fat, 0 mg Chol, 187 mg Sod, 43 g Carb, 40 g Sugar, 0 g Fib, 3 g Prot, 2 mg Calc.

For Your Information

Ginger, bitter orange, or grapefruit marmalade would also be terrific in these soufflés. You can also opt for almost any jam; one that contains pieces of fruit will give you a better texture and more flavor.

EASY MARMALADE SOUFFLÉS

triple chocolate pudding

SERVES 6

½ cup packed dark brown sugar

⅓ cup unsweetened cocoa powder

2 ½ tablespoons cornstarch

2 ounces semisweet chocolate, finely chopped

Pinch salt

2 cups fat-free chocolate milk

½ teaspoon vanilla extract

1 Combine brown sugar, cocoa, cornstarch, chocolate, and salt in medium saucepan. Whisk in 1 cup chocolate milk. Set pan over medium heat and cook, whisking frequently, until chocolate has melted and mixture is smooth, about 4 minutes. Add remaining 1 cup chocolate milk and cook, whisking frequently, until large bubbles pop on surface and pudding is thick and smooth, about 10 minutes.

2 Remove pan from heat and stir in vanilla. Pour evenly into 6 (6-ounce) custard cups, ramekins, or stemmed glasses. Serve warm or at room temperature, or cover and refrigerate at least 2 hours and serve chilled.

Per serving (scant ½ cup): 191 Cal, 4 g Total Fat, 2 g Sat Fat, 0 g Trans Fat, 1 mg Chol, 79 mg Sod, 40 g Carb, 33 g Sugar, 2 g Fib, 4 g Prot, 112 mg Calc.

Stay On Track

Serve the pudding in bowls or in stemmed glasses topped with raspberries, sliced strawberries, or thinly sliced nectarines—it will look and taste wonderful.

bourbon butterscotch pudding
SERVES 6

⅔ cup packed dark brown sugar

2 tablespoons cornstarch

2 cups fat-free milk

3 large egg yolks

⅛ teaspoon salt

1 tablespoon bourbon

6 tablespoons fat-free whipped topping

Freshly grated nutmeg

1 Whisk together brown sugar and cornstarch in medium saucepan. Slowly whisk in milk until smooth. Cook over medium heat, whisking constantly, until mixture bubbles and thickens, 8–10 minutes. Remove saucepan from heat.

2 Whisk together egg yolks and salt in medium bowl. Whisk about ½ cup of the hot milk mixture into egg mixture. Return mixture to saucepan and cook, stirring, over low heat until smooth and thickened, 1–2 minutes.

3 Pour pudding through sieve set over medium bowl. Whisk in bourbon. Divide pudding evenly among 6 dessert dishes. Immediately place piece of wax paper directly onto surface of each pudding to prevent skin from forming. Refrigerate until thoroughly chilled and set, at least 2 hours.

4 Remove wax paper, and top each pudding with a dollop of whipped topping and a sprinkle of nutmeg.

Per serving (½ cup pudding and 1 tablespoon topping):
171 Cal, 2 g Total Fat, 1 g Sat Fat, 0 g Trans Fat, 107 mg Chol, 96 mg Sod, 32 g Carb, 28 g Sugar, 0 g Fib, 4 g Prot, 133 mg Calc.

Make Ahead
The pudding can be made through step 3 and refrigerated up to 3 days. When ready to serve, continue with step 4.

COOKING WITH KIDS

Wondering how to expand your children's food and flavor world? Getting them involved in meal prep can be a great place to start. Most kids are excited about contributing to a meal and are much more likely to try a new food if they had a hand in making it. What's more, spending time together in the kitchen can be a great way to bond, even on busy weeknights. Here are some suggestions for age-appropriate tasks you can set them up with.

Toddlers (ages 2 to 4) Young children are beginning to master hand and finger control and take pride in completing simple tasks. They may enjoy:

- Rinsing fruits and vegetables and patting them dry.
- Sprinkling toppings onto pizzas or casseroles.
- Layering ingredients into sandwiches.
- Tearing salad greens into small pieces with their hands.
- Pulling parsley and cilantro leaves off their stems.
- Peeling the skins from fruits like oranges and bananas.
- Shucking corn on the cob.
- Wiping the counter with a sponge.

Kids (ages 5 to 9) At these ages, kids are mastering basic math, developing arm strength, and increasing their attention spans. They may even be able to read parts of a recipe. They can help by:

- Measuring out dry and liquid ingredients.
- Breaking eggs into a bowl.
- Snipping herbs with kids' safety scissors.
- Cutting soft fruits like bananas and strawberries with a plastic knife.
- Juicing lemons and limes.
- Spooning muffin or cupcake batter into pans.
- Spreading soft foods such as hummus, peanut butter, or cream cheese and icing and decorating cupcakes.
- Setting the table.

Preteens (ages 10 to 12) In addition to being able to plan simple meals on their own, most preteens can read through a recipe. With some assistance, they can accomplish many tasks, including:

- Separating eggs.
- Slicing soft foods such as mushrooms, cheese, and pitted olives with a plastic knife.
- Shredding cheese and vegetables with a box grater.
- Hand-forming foods like meatballs and hamburgers.
- Layering foods into casseroles.
- Rolling out pizza dough.

PITCH IN!

Here are our top recommendations for family-project meals and delicious treats to share.

Bacon-and-Swiss Coddled Eggs
p 7

Breakfast Pizza
p 16

Whole-Grain Blueberry Muffins with Lemon Crumb Topping
p 17

Piña Colada Breakfast Cups
p 25

Chicken Wraps with Tangy Slaw
p 32

Marinated Cherry Salad with Rosemary Ham
p 51

Spaghetti Squash with Garden Meatballs
p 66

Spaghetti with Mozzarella-Stuffed Meatballs
p 99

Easy Garden Vegetable Lasagna
p 116

Mac-and-Cheese Muffins
p 121

Greek Pasta Salad
p 122

Mushroom and Arugula Pizza
p 128

Three-Cheese Polenta Pizza with Fresh Tomatoes
p 129

Mediterranean Meat Loaf with Roast Tomatoes
p 138

Crispy Chicken Fingers with Sweet Ginger Sauce
p 141

Easy Chicken Parmesan with Basil
p 165

Rich Chocolate–Beet Cake Squares
p 214

Chocolate Cupcakes with Coconut-Pecan Frosting
p 215

Lemon-Poppy Seed Cupcakes
p 216

Lemony Angel Meringue
p 220

Raspberry Shortcakes with Greek Yogurt
p 225

Chocolate, Vanilla, and Hazelnut Ice-Cream Terrine
p 233

Peanut Butter–Oatmeal Chocolate Chip Cookies
p 236

Almond Blondie Bars
p 238

**CHOCOLATE, VANILLA,
AND HAZELNUT
ICE-CREAM TERRINE**

chocolate, vanilla, and hazelnut ice-cream terrine

SERVES 12

1 ¼ cups chopped hazelnuts

4 ounces semisweet chocolate, chopped

½ cup fat-free half-and-half

¼ cup packed dark brown sugar

Pinch salt

½ teaspoon vanilla extract

4 cups chocolate fat-free ice cream, softened

2 cups vanilla fat-free ice cream, softened

1 Preheat oven to 350°F. Toast hazelnuts on large baking sheet until golden brown and fragrant, 6–8 minutes. Process ¾ cup hazelnuts in food processor until nuts form a smooth paste, 3–5 minutes. Add chocolate and pulse until chocolate is finely ground or melted, about 1 minute. Leave in food processor.

2 Bring half-and-half, brown sugar, and salt just to boil in small saucepan over medium heat, stirring to dissolve sugar. With motor running, slowly pour half-and-half mixture through feed tube of food processor. Blend until mixture is very smooth, 3–4 minutes. Transfer to bowl; stir in vanilla and let cool to room temperature. Refrigerate, covered, until ready to use.

3 Line 5 x 9-inch loaf pan with 2 sheets of plastic wrap, extending wrap over rim of pan by 2 inches. With rubber spatula, evenly spread 2 cups chocolate ice cream in pan, making sure to spread it into corners. Spread ½ cup hazelnut mixture evenly over chocolate ice cream; freeze 15 minutes. Layer with 2 cups vanilla ice cream, then ½ cup hazelnut mixture; freeze 15 minutes. Layer with remaining 2 cups chocolate ice cream, then remaining ½ cup hazelnut mixture. Press remaining ½ cup chopped hazelnuts into top. Fold over plastic wrap to cover and freeze until firm, at least 4 hours.

4 Lift terrine from pan with plastic wrap. Remove wrap. Cut terrine into 12 slices with serrated knife dipped into hot water and wiped dry after each cut. Serve at once.

Per serving (1 slice terrine): 253 Cal, 13 g Total Fat, 3 g Sat Fat, 0 g Trans Fat, 5 mg Chol, 72 mg Sod, 35 g Carb, 25 g Sugar, 3 g Fib, 6 g Prot, 117 mg Calc.

cranberry-buttermilk sorbet

SERVES 8

1 ¼ cups sugar

1 ¼ cups water

▲ 2 cups fresh or frozen cranberries

1 cup low-fat buttermilk

½ cup orange juice

2 teaspoons finely grated orange zest

1 teaspoon vanilla extract

1 Combine sugar and water in medium saucepan over medium-high heat and bring to boil, stirring until sugar has dissolved. Add cranberries and return to boil. Reduce heat and simmer, stirring occasionally, until cranberries pop and soften, about 5 minutes. Let cool 5 minutes.

2 Transfer cranberry mixture to food processor or blender and puree. Pour cranberry mixture through sieve set over large bowl, pressing hard on solids to extract as much liquid as possible. Add buttermilk, orange juice and zest, and vanilla to cranberry mixture. Cover and refrigerate until thoroughly chilled, about 3 hours.

3 Pour mixture into ice-cream maker and freeze according to manufacturer's instructions. Transfer sorbet to freezer container and freeze until firm, at least 2 hours.

Per serving (½ cup): 108 Cal, 0 g Total Fat, 0 g Sat Fat, 0 g Trans Fat, 1 mg Chol, 34 mg Sod, 29 g Carb, 25 g Sugar, 1 g Fib, 1 g Prot, 41 mg Calc.

Stay On Track

For a wonderfully healthful dessert, serve this sorbet over a colorful salad made of diced citrus fruits and raspberries.

zingy berry gelatin mold

SERVES 8

2 ½ cups water

4 Red Zinger tea bags

2 tablespoons unflavored gelatin

3 cups blueberries, raspberries, or blackberries, or a combination of berries

1 Bring water to boil in medium saucepan over high heat. Remove pan from heat. Add tea bags, cover, and steep 5 minutes. Remove and discard tea bags.

2 Pour ½ cup tea into small bowl and let cool slightly. Sprinkle with gelatin and let soften 5 minutes. Pour gelatin mixture into tea and cook over low heat, stirring, until gelatin has dissolved. Let cool to room temperature.

3 Place berries in 4 x 8 ½-inch loaf pan or 1-quart decorative mold. Pour tea over berries and press berries down to submerge. Cover top with plastic wrap and refrigerate until set, at least 3 hours or up to 2 days.

4 To serve, run table knife around inside of pan and dip bottom of pan in hot water for 5 seconds; invert pan onto serving platter and shake to release terrine. With a serrated knife, cut terrine crosswise into 16 slices. Place 2 slices on each plate and serve.

Per serving (2 slices): 38 Cal, 0 g Total Fat, 0 g Sat Fat, 0 g Trans Fat, 0 mg Chol, 4 mg Sod, 8 g Carb, 6 g Sugar, 1 g Fib, 2 g Prot, 4 mg Calc.

For Your Information

You could use any herb tea in this recipe, but we like Red Zinger because of its stunning crimson color and its flavors of peppermint, lemongrass, and orange, which complement the berries nicely.

peanut butter-oatmeal chocolate chip cookies

MAKES 30

1 cup old-fashioned oats

1 cup packed light brown sugar

1 cup well-stirred reduced-fat natural peanut butter, at room temperature

3 tablespoons unsalted butter, at room temperature

▲ ½ cup fat-free egg substitute

1 teaspoon vanilla extract

¼ teaspoon salt

1 cup all-purpose flour

½ cup miniature semisweet chocolate chips

1 Preheat oven to 375°F. Pulse oats in food processor until finely ground. Add brown sugar and pulse until combined.

2 With electric mixer on low speed, beat peanut butter and butter in large bowl until light and fluffy, about 2 minutes. Add egg substitute, vanilla, and salt, and beat until combined. Add oat mixture and beat until combined. With rubber spatula, stir in flour and chocolate chips.

3 Drop dough by rounded tablespoons, about 2 inches apart, onto ungreased baking sheet. Using a fork, flatten to about 3/8-inch thick, leaving imprint on tops. Bake cookies until golden brown, about 16 minutes. Let cool on baking sheet on wire rack 1 minute. Transfer cookies to racks and let cool completely. Repeat with remaining cookie dough.

Per serving (1 cookie): 130 Cal, 5 g Total Fat, 2 g Sat Fat, 0 g Trans Fat, 3 mg Chol, 95 mg Sod, 18 g Carb, 10 g Sugar, 1 g Fib, 3 g Prot, 9 mg Calc.

ALMOND BLONDIE BARS p 238

ORANGE, CORIANDER, AND CORNMEAL BISCOTTI p 239

PEANUT BUTTER–OATMEAL CHOCOLATE CHIP COOKIES

almond blondie bars

MAKES 16

⅓ cup + ½ cup sliced almonds

⅔ cup whole wheat flour

½ teaspoon baking powder

¼ teaspoon salt

¼ cup well-stirred natural almond butter

3 tablespoons unsalted butter

¾ cup packed light brown sugar

▲ ¼ cup fat-free egg substitute

1 teaspoon vanilla extract

1 Preheat oven to 350°F. Line 8-inch square baking pan with foil, extending foil over rim of pan by 2 inches; spray foil with nonstick spray.

2 Pulse ⅓ cup almonds in food processor until finely ground. Add flour, baking powder, and salt, and pulse until combined; transfer to small bowl. Heat almond butter and butter in small saucepan over low heat, stirring until butter melts. Transfer mixture to medium bowl; with rubber spatula, stir in brown sugar until smooth. Stir in egg substitute and vanilla. Add flour mixture and stir just until blended. Stir in ¼ cup almonds.

3 Scrape batter into prepared pan and spread evenly; top with remaining ¼ cup almonds. Bake until toothpick inserted in center comes out with moist crumbs, 30–35 minutes. Let cool in pan on rack 15 minutes. Lift from pan using foil and let cool completely on rack. Remove foil and cut into 16 bars.

Per serving (1 bar): 131 Cal, 7 g Total Fat, 2 g Sat Fat, 0 g Trans Fat, 6 mg Chol, 81 mg Sod, 16 g Carb, 10 g Sugar, 1 g Fib, 3 g Prot, 39 mg Calc.

Make Ahead

Place the bars in an airtight container with wax paper between layers and store at room temperature up to 3 days, or freeze up to 3 months. If frozen, thaw at room temperature overnight.

orange, coriander, and cornmeal biscotti

MAKES 60

1 ½ cups all-purpose flour

▲ 1 ½ cups yellow cornmeal

¾ cup packed light brown sugar

2 teaspoons baking powder

1 ½ teaspoons finely grated orange zest

1 teaspoon ground coriander

½ teaspoon salt

½ cup water

▲ ½ cup fat-free egg substitute

½ teaspoon vanilla extract

¾ cup sliced almonds

1 Preheat oven to 325°F. Line large baking sheet with parchment paper.

2 Whisk together flour, cornmeal, brown sugar, baking powder, orange zest, coriander, and salt in large bowl; break up any lumps of brown sugar with your hands. Combine water, egg substitute, and vanilla in small bowl and stir into flour mixture; mixture will be very soft and sticky. Stir in almonds.

3 Divide dough into 3 equal pieces. On floured surface, roll each piece in flour to coat, then shape each into 10-inch log. Transfer logs to prepared baking sheet, placing about 3 inches apart. Bake until firm when pressed, about 45 minutes. Let logs cool on baking sheet on rack at least 30 minutes.

4 Position racks in middle and upper third of oven. Transfer one log at a time to cutting board. With serrated knife, cut each log into 20 slices ½-inch-thick diagonal slices. Place slices in single layer on 2 large baking sheets. Bake until golden brown, rotating pans halfway through baking, about 15 minutes. Turn cookies over and bake until golden brown and very dry, 10–15 minutes. Let biscotti cool completely on pans on racks.

Per serving (3 cookies): 133 Cal, 2 g Total Fat, 0 g Sat Fat, 0 g Trans Fat, 0 mg Chol, 125 mg Sod, 26 g Carb, 8 g Sugar, 1 g Fib, 3 g Prot, 30 mg Calc.

Make Ahead
Place the cooled biscotti in an airtight container and store at room temperature up to 2 weeks.

Chapter 9

holiday classics

holiday classics

thanksgiving
Fennel-Spiced Roast Turkey with Mushroom Gravy 243
Creamed Spinach and Pearl Onion Gratin 244
Mashed Sweet Potatoes with Maple Brown Butter and Sage 245

christmas
Apple-and-Spinach Salad with Hazelnut Dressing 246
Bourbon-Glazed Ham with Golden Raisin Sauce 247
Roasted Brussels Sprouts with Walnuts and Bacon 250
Whipped Potato-and-Parsnip Puree 251

new year's eve cocktail party
Pear-Gingersnap Punch 252
Balsamic-Glazed Melon with Prosciutto 253
Classic Salmon Mousse 254
Crispy Root Vegetable Chips 255

passover
Caramelized Onion and Garlic Soup 256
Cider-Braised Slow-Cooker Brisket 257
Orange-Apricot Haroset 258
Potato-Zucchini Kugel 259

OTHER FESTIVE MENUS 260

easter
Minted Pea Soup 261
Roast Spring Lamb with Lavender and Honey 262
Lemony Roast Potato and Green Bean Medley 263

july fourth
Citrus Chicken Under a Brick 264
Slow-Cooker Smoky BBQ Beans 265
Herb-and-Parmesan Grilled Corn on the Cob 268

fennel-spiced roast turkey with mushroom gravy

SERVES 12

1 (10- to 12-pound) turkey

1 tablespoon fennel seeds

1 tablespoon chopped fresh thyme

2 garlic cloves, minced

3 teaspoons olive oil

1 ¼ teaspoons salt

▲ 1 ¾ cups reduced-sodium chicken broth

¼ cup dry sherry

▲ ½ pound shiitake mushrooms, stems discarded, caps sliced

2 tablespoons all-purpose flour

1 Place oven rack in lower third of oven. Preheat oven to 450°F. Remove neck and giblets from cavity of turkey and discard (or save for another use). Rinse turkey inside and out; pat dry with paper towels.

2 Pulse fennel seeds, thyme, garlic, 1 teaspoon oil, and ¾ teaspoon salt in mini–food processor or spice grinder until paste forms. Carefully separate skin from turkey breast and rub fennel mixture evenly on meat. Tuck wing tips under bird. Tie turkey legs together with kitchen string. Place turkey, breast side up, in large roasting pan fitted with rack. Pour 1 cup broth into bottom of pan; roast turkey 20 minutes. Reduce oven temperature to 350°F. Roast until instant-read thermometer inserted into thickest part of thigh (not touching bone) registers 165°F, about 2 ½ hours longer. Transfer turkey to cutting board. Cover loosely with foil and let stand 30 minutes.

3 Meanwhile, to make gravy, pour drippings and juices from roasting pan into large glass measuring cup. Let stand 5 minutes; then skim off fat and discard. Add remaining ¾ cup broth and sherry into skimmed pan drippings. Heat remaining 2 teaspoons oil in large skillet over medium heat. Add mushrooms and remaining ½ teaspoon salt, and cook, stirring occasionally, until mushrooms are tender, about 5 minutes. Stir in flour; cook, stirring, 1 minute. Add sherry mixture and cook, stirring frequently, until gravy thickens, 4–5 minutes.

4 Discard turkey skin. Carve breast and thigh meat into 24 slices (save drumsticks and wings for another use). Serve with gravy.

Per serving (2 slices turkey without skin and 3 tablespoons gravy): 347 Cal, 6 g Total Fat, 2 g Sat Fat, 0 g Trans Fat, 166 mg Chol, 434 mg Sod, 5 g Carb, 1 g Sugar, 1 g Fib, 64 g Prot, 43 mg Calc.

creamed spinach and pearl onion gratin

SERVES 8

4 teaspoons olive oil

2 garlic cloves, minced

2 tablespoons all-purpose flour

▲ 2 cups fat-free milk

½ teaspoon salt

Pinch ground nutmeg

2 tablespoons grated Parmesan cheese

▲ 1 cup thawed frozen pearl onions

▲ 2 (11-ounce) containers baby spinach

½ cup shredded reduced-fat Swiss cheese

1 Preheat oven to 375°F. Spray 1 ½-quart baking dish with nonstick spray.

2 Heat 2 teaspoons oil in medium saucepan over medium-high heat. Add garlic and cook until fragrant, about 30 seconds. Add flour and cook, stirring constantly, 1 minute. Whisk in milk, salt, and nutmeg; bring to boil. Reduce heat and simmer, whisking occasionally, until mixture thickens, 6–8 minutes. Remove from heat; stir in Parmesan. Cover sauce and set aside.

3 Heat remaining 2 teaspoons oil in large skillet over medium heat. Add pearl onions and cook, stirring occasionally, until softened and lightly browned, about 5 minutes. Transfer to bowl. Add spinach, in batches, and cook, stirring occasionally, until spinach is wilted, about 8 minutes. Drain any liquid remaining in skillet. Stir in sauce and pearl onions.

4 Spoon into baking dish. Sprinkle with Swiss cheese. Bake until topping is browned and bubbling, about 15 minutes. Let stand 10 minutes before serving.

Per serving (½ cup): 110 Cal, 3 g Total Fat, 1 g Sat Fat, 0 g Trans Fat, 5 mg Chol, 335 mg Sod, 16 g Carb, 3 g Sugar, 4 g Fib, 7 g Prot, 212 mg Calc.

Make Ahead

You can assemble and bake this gratin up to 3 days ahead. Cool it completely on a wire rack; cover the top with foil and refrigerate. When ready to serve, reheat the covered gratin in a preheated 325°F oven until hot, about 30 minutes.

mashed sweet potatoes with maple brown butter and sage

SERVES 8

- 4 (12-ounce) sweet potatoes, peeled and cut into 2-inch pieces
- ¼ cup fat-free milk
- ¾ teaspoon cinnamon
- ½ teaspoon salt
- Pinch ground nutmeg
- 2 tablespoons unsalted butter
- 1 tablespoon maple syrup
- 2 teaspoons chopped fresh sage

1 Put potatoes in large saucepan with enough water to cover by 2 inches; bring to boil over high heat. Reduce heat and simmer until potatoes are tender, about 20 minutes; drain. Return potatoes to saucepan. Add milk, cinnamon, salt, and nutmeg; mash with potato masher or large fork until fluffy.

2 Melt butter in small skillet over medium heat. Cook, stirring, until butter just begins to turn light brown, about 2 minutes. Remove from heat; stir in maple syrup and sage.

3 Reheat potatoes over low heat if necessary. Transfer to serving bowl and drizzle with melted butter mixture.

Per serving (½ cup potatoes and 1 teaspoon maple butter): 141 Cal, 3 g Total Fat, 2 g Sat Fat, 0 g Trans Fat, 8 mg Chol, 217 mg Sod, 27 g Carb, 7 g Sugar, 4 g Fib, 2 g Prot, 52 mg Calc.

For Your Information

The terms "yam" and "sweet potato" are often used interchangeably, although true yams are a type of tropical tuber that are not often sold in the United States. Whether your grocery store calls them yams or sweet potatoes, choose a variety with bright orange flesh for the sweetest flavor.

apple-and-spinach salad with hazelnut dressing

SERVES 8

¼ cup hazelnuts

3 tablespoons balsamic vinegar

1 tablespoon honey

4 teaspoons hazelnut oil

½ teaspoon salt

¼ teaspoon black pepper

▲ 8 cups baby spinach

▲ 4 cups torn frisée

▲ 3 red apples, cored and thinly sliced

1 Preheat oven to 325°F.

2 Place hazelnuts on small baking sheet. Bake, stirring once, until toasted, about 10 minutes. Wrap hot hazelnuts in clean kitchen towel and rub nuts with towel to remove as much of the skins as possible. Chop hazelnuts.

3 Combine vinegar, honey, oil, salt, and pepper in large bowl; whisk until blended. Add spinach, frisée, and apples to dressing; toss to coat. Divide salad among 8 plates and sprinkle ½ tablespoon hazelnuts on each serving.

Per serving (1 ½ cups salad and ½ tablespoon nuts):
110 Cal, 5 g Total Fat, 0 g Sat Fat, 0 g Trans Fat, 0 mg Chol, 192 mg Sod, 17 g Carb, 10 g Sugar, 4 g Fib, 2 g Prot, 41 mg Calc.

Stay On Track
Pomegranate seeds make a crunchy, antioxidant-packed garnish for this festive salad.

bourbon-glazed ham with golden raisin sauce

SERVES 14

½ cup orange marmalade fruit spread

1 tablespoon Dijon mustard

1 tablespoon bourbon

1 (3-pound) low-sodium lean boneless fully cooked ham

1 cup orange juice

1 cup golden raisins

2 tablespoons cider vinegar

1 tablespoon packed brown sugar

2 teaspoons cornstarch

Pinch salt

Thyme sprigs for garnish (optional)

1 Combine ¼ cup fruit spread, mustard, and bourbon in small bowl. Brush glaze over ham. Spray sheet of foil with nonstick spray and loosely cover ham, coated side down, with foil. Bake until ham is heated through and instant-read thermometer inserted into center registers 140°F, about 30 minutes. Transfer ham to cutting board. Let stand 10 minutes.

2 Meanwhile to make golden raisin sauce, combine orange juice and raisins in medium saucepan; let stand until raisins are plump, about 10 minutes. Add remaining ¼ cup fruit spread, vinegar, brown sugar, cornstarch, and salt; bring to boil over medium-high heat. Reduce heat and simmer, stirring occasionally, until sauce thickens, about 4 minutes. Transfer to a serving bowl.

3 Cut ham into 14 (½-inch-thick) slices and serve with sauce. Garnish with thyme (if using).

Per serving (1 slice ham with 2 tablespoons sauce): 221 Cal, 5 g Total Fat, 2 g Sat Fat, 0 g Trans Fat, 51 mg Chol, 981 mg Sod, 20 g Carb, 15 g Sugar, 1 g Fib, 21 g Prot, 16 mg Calc.

**GOLDEN RAISI
SAUCE** p 247

**WHIPPED POTATO-AND-
PARSNIP PUREE** p 251

**ROASTED BRUSSELS
SPROUTS WITH WALNUTS
AND BACON** p 250

**APPLE-AND-SPINACH
SALAD WITH HAZELNUT
DRESSING** p 246

**BOURBON-GLAZED
HAM** p 247

roasted brussels sprouts with walnuts and bacon

SERVES 8

christmas

- ▲ **2 pints Brussels sprouts, halved**

- **4 shallots, halved**

- **1 tablespoon olive oil**

- **½ teaspoon salt**

- **½ teaspoon black pepper**

- **4 slices turkey bacon, coarsely chopped**

- **¼ cup toasted walnuts, coarsely chopped**

1 Preheat oven to 450°F. Place Brussels sprouts and shallots on large baking sheet. Drizzle with oil and sprinkle with salt and pepper; toss to coat. Spread evenly in pan. Roast until Brussels sprouts and shallots are tender, 20–25 minutes, stirring once halfway through cooking time.

2 Meanwhile, spray small skillet with nonstick spray and set over medium-high heat. Add bacon and cook, stirring frequently, until crisp, 3–4 minutes. Transfer to paper towels to drain.

3 Transfer Brussels sprouts and shallots to serving bowl. Sprinkle with bacon and top with walnuts.

Per serving (½ cup): 89 Cal, 6 g Total Fat, 1 g Sat Fat, 0 g Trans Fat, 7 mg Chol, 317 mg Sod, 6 g Carb, 1 g Sugar, 2 g Fib, 4 g Prot, 25 mg Calc.

Stay On Track

If you'd like to incorporate even more veggies into this dish, add a diced red bell pepper to the baking sheet along with the Brussels sprouts and shallots.

whipped potato-and-parsnip puree
SERVES 8

- ▲ 1 ¾ pounds russet potatoes, peeled and cut into quarters
- ▲ ½ pound parsnips, peeled and cut into 2-inch pieces
- ½ cup low-fat buttermilk
- ▲ ⅓ cup fat-free half-and-half
- 1 tablespoon unsalted butter, softened
- ½ teaspoon salt
- ¼ teaspoon ground white pepper
- 2 teaspoons chopped fresh chives

1 Put potatoes and parsnips in large saucepan with enough water to cover by 2 inches; bring to boil over high heat. Reduce heat and simmer until very tender, about 20 minutes; drain.

2 Return potatoes and parsnips to saucepan. Add buttermilk, half-and-half, butter, salt, and white pepper; mash with potato masher or large fork until fluffy. Sprinkle with chives.

Per serving (½ cup): 114 Cal, 2 g Total Fat, 1 g Sat Fat, 0 g Trans Fat, 4 mg Chol, 173 mg Sod, 24 g Carb, 5 g Sugar, 3 g Fib, 4 g Prot, 57 mg Calc.

Make Ahead
You can refrigerate the cooled puree up to 3 days. To reheat, transfer the puree to a saucepan. Cover and cook over medium heat, stirring occasionally, until heated through; stir in water if the puree is too thick.

pear-gingersnap punch

SERVES 12

¼ cup lemon juice

2 tablespoons sugar

1 cup water

2 cinnamon sticks

10 whole cloves

4 cups pear nectar

3 tablespoons
cinnamon-flavored liqueur

1 tablespoon grated peeled
fresh ginger

1 Combine lemon juice, sugar, and water in large saucepan. Tie cinnamon sticks and cloves together in small piece of cheesecloth and add to pan. Set over medium-high heat and bring to simmer. Cook, stirring occasionally, until flavors are infused, about 5 minutes. Remove from heat and discard spices. Stir in pear nectar, liqueur, and ginger.

2 Pour into tall ice-filled glasses and serve at once.

Per serving (⅔ cup): 71 Cal, 0 g Total Fat, 0 g Sat Fat, 0 g Trans Fat, 0 mg Chol, 5 mg Sod, 17 g Carb, 6 g Sugar, 1 g Fib, 0 g Prot, 5 mg Calc.

For Your Information
For a nonalcoholic version of this cocktail, substitute 3 tablespoons cinnamon coffee-flavoring syrup for the liqueur. Or, to add more kick, add 3 tablespoons (1 jigger) of light rum to each drink for an additional **3 PointsPlus** values per serving.

balsamic-glazed melon with prosciutto

SERVES 8

1 cup balsamic vinegar

1 tablespoon maple syrup

2 ½ cups cantaloupe cubes

2 ½ cups honeydew melon cubes

8 thin slices lean prosciutto, halved

1 To make glaze, combine vinegar and maple syrup in medium saucepan; bring to boil over medium-high heat. Boil until mixture is reduced to a syrupy glaze, about 8 minutes. Remove saucepan from heat; set aside to cool.

2 Meanwhile, thread cantaloupe, honeydew, and prosciutto alternately on 16 (6-inch) bamboo skewers. Serve skewers drizzled with glaze.

Per serving (2 skewers with 1 ½ tablespoons glaze):
101 Cal, 2 g Total Fat, 1 g Sat Fat, 0 g Trans Fat, 11 mg Chol, 400 mg Sod, 17 g Carb, 14 g Sugar, 1 g Fib, 5 g Prot, 18 mg Calc.

Stay On Track
If you like, add bite-size cubes of mozzarella to the skewers. A ½-ounce cube of fat-free mozzarella per skewer will increase the per-serving *PointsPlus* value by **1**.

classic salmon mousse

SERVES 16

new year's eve cocktail party

- ▲ **1 (14.75-ounce) can wild salmon, drained**
- ▲ **1 cup plain fat-free Greek yogurt**
- **½ cup fat-free mayonnaise**
- ▲ **½ small onion, grated**
- **Grated zest and juice of 1 lemon**
- **3 tablespoons chopped fresh dill**
- **¼ teaspoon salt**
- **⅓ cup cold water**
- **1 envelope unflavored gelatin**
- ▲ **1 large bunch watercress, tough stems removed**
- ▲ **1 cucumber, thinly sliced**

1 Pulse salmon, yogurt, mayonnaise, onion, lemon zest and juice, dill, and salt in food processor until pureed.

2 Place water in small microwavable bowl and sprinkle with gelatin; let stand until gelatin softens, about 5 minutes. Microwave on High until gelatin completely dissolves, 10–15 seconds. Add to salmon mixture and pulse to combine.

3 Spray 4 x 8-inch loaf pan with cooking spray; line with plastic wrap. Scrape salmon mixture into prepared pan and level top; cover with plastic wrap. Refrigerate until set, at least 6 hours.

4 To serve, unmold mousse onto serving plate and remove plastic wrap. Surround mousse with watercress and cucumber slices.

Per serving (¼ cup mousse and about ⅓ cup watercress and cucumber): 70 Cal, 3 g Total Fat, 1 g Sat Fat, 0 g Trans Fat, 17 mg Chol, 224 mg Sod, 3 g Carb, 2 g Sugar, 0 g Fib, 8 g Prot, 64 mg Calc.

Make Ahead

You can prepare this appetizer through step 3 up to 2 days ahead and keep it refrigerated. Unmold and serve as directed in step 4.

crispy root vegetable chips
SERVES 8

▲ **1 very large carrot, scrubbed**

▲ **1 very large parsnip, peeled**

▲ **1 small sweet potato, scrubbed**

1 teaspoon canola oil

2 teaspoons grated lemon zest

½ teaspoon kosher salt

Pinch cayenne

1 Preheat oven to 375°F.

2 Slice carrot, parsnip, and sweet potato into $1/16$-inch-thick slices using mandoline or slicing attachment of food processor. Place vegetables in large bowl. Add oil, lemon zest, salt, and cayenne; toss to coat.

3 Arrange vegetables in single layer on 2 large rimmed baking sheets. Bake until well browned, 30–35 minutes, rotating baking sheets halfway through baking. Check vegetables often during last 10 minutes of baking and transfer to large bowl as they brown. Chips will crisp as they cool.

Per serving (about ½ cup): 37 Cal, 1 g Total Fat, 0 g Sat Fat, 0 g Trans Fat, 0 mg Chol, 137 mg Sod, 8 g Carb, 2 g Sugar, 1 g Fib, 1 g Prot, 16 mg Calc.

Make Ahead
You can store the chips in an airtight container at room temperature up to 3 days. If the chips lose their crispness, place them on a baking sheet and bake at 250°F for 5 to 10 minutes.

new year's eve cocktail party

caramelized onion and garlic soup

SERVES 8

- **2 garlic bulbs**
- ▲ **2 pounds onions, each cut into 6 wedges**
- **4 teaspoons olive oil**
- **1 teaspoon salt**
- **½ teaspoon black pepper**
- **½ cup dry white wine**
- ▲ **2 (32-ounce) cartons reduced-sodium beef broth**
- **4 fresh thyme sprigs**
- **2 tablespoons finely chopped fresh parsley**

1 Preheat oven to 350°F. Spray large roasting pan with nonstick spray.

2 Cut garlic bulbs in half crosswise. Wrap garlic in foil; place on one side of roasting pan. Add onions to pan. Drizzle with oil and sprinkle with salt and pepper; toss to coat. Spread onions evenly in pan. Bake, stirring onions occasionally, until onions are browned and tender and garlic is softened, about 1 hour. Let garlic stand until cool enough to handle.

3 Transfer onions to large pot. Squeeze out garlic pulp and add to pot.

4 Set roasting pan over medium-high heat. Add wine and cook, scraping any browned bits from bottom of pan. Add wine mixture, broth, and thyme to pot. Bring to boil. Reduce heat and simmer, covered, 30 minutes. Let mixture cool 5 minutes. Remove and discard thyme sprigs.

5 Puree, in batches, in food processor or blender. Return soup to pot. Cook over medium heat until heated through, about 4 minutes. Sprinkle with parsley.

Per serving (1 cup): 116 Cal, 4 g Total Fat, 1 g Sat Fat, 0 g Trans Fat, 0 mg Chol, 359 mg Sod, 13 g Total Carb, 8 g Total Sugar, 3 g Fib, 6 g Prot, 55 mg Calc.

cider-braised slow-cooker brisket

SERVES 8

1 (3-pound) lean center-cut beef brisket, trimmed

¾ teaspoon salt

½ teaspoon black pepper

2 teaspoons olive oil

▲ 1 large onion, thinly sliced

▲ 3 celery stalks, sliced

▲ 2 carrots, sliced

2 teaspoons chopped fresh thyme

¾ cup apple cider

1 tablespoon cider vinegar

1 tablespoon potato starch

2 tablespoons cold water

1 Sprinkle brisket with salt and pepper. Heat 1 teaspoon oil in large skillet over medium-high heat. Add brisket and cook, turning occasionally, until browned, about 8 minutes. Transfer beef to 5- or 6-quart slow cooker.

2 Add remaining 1 teaspoon oil to skillet and place over medium-high heat. Add onion, celery, carrots, and thyme; cook, stirring frequently, until vegetables are softened, about 8 minutes. Add apple cider and vinegar; bring to boil. Pour onion mixture over beef in slow cooker. Cover and cook until beef and vegetables are fork-tender, 3–4 hours on high or 6–8 hours on low.

3 About 25 minutes before end of cooking time, skim fat from sauce in slow cooker. Mix potato starch and water in small bowl until smooth; stir into slow cooker. Cover and cook on high until mixture simmers and thickens, 20–25 minutes.

4 Transfer brisket to cutting board. Cut brisket across grain into 24 slices and serve with sauce.

Per serving (3 slices brisket and ¼ cup sauce): 305 Cal, 10 g Total Fat, 4 g Sat Fat, 0 g Trans Fat, 88 mg Chol, 322 mg Sod, 8 g Carb, 4 g Sugar, 1 g Fib, 43 g Prot, 39 mg Calc.

Make Ahead

You can make the beef through step 3 and refrigerate it up to 4 days. To do so, cool it completely and place the beef and sauce in an airtight container. Reheat in a large skillet until heated through. Add a few tablespoons of water, if needed. Proceed with step 4.

orange-apricot haroset

SERVES 8

- ▲ **2 seedless navel oranges, peeled and cut into ½-inch pieces**
- **½ cup dried apricots**
- **½ cup pitted dates**
- **½ cup sliced almonds**
- **¼ cup Malaga or other sweet wine**
- **2 teaspoons lemon juice**
- **1 teaspoon honey**
- **¾ teaspoon cinnamon**

Combine all ingredients in food processor and pulse until finely chopped. Transfer to airtight container and refrigerate at least 1 hour or up to 24 hours to allow flavors to blend.

Per serving (scant ¼ cup): 115 Cal, 3 g Total Fat, 0 g Sat Fat, 0 g Trans Fat, 0 mg Chol, 2 mg Sod, 21 g Carb, 16 g Sugar, 3 g Fib, 2 g Prot, 43 mg Calc.

Stay On Track

This classic Passover dish is delicious on its own, but it's most often eaten on matzo. For a **0 PointsPlus** value serving option, spoon it into endive leaves. If you like, top it with a dollop of its Passover condiment partner, pickled horseradish.

potato-zucchini kugel

SERVES 8

- 4 russet potatoes
- 4 garlic cloves, minced
- 2 teaspoons olive oil
- 1 onion, thinly sliced
- 1 medium zucchini, grated
- ½ cup reduced-sodium chicken broth
- 2 large eggs, lightly beaten
- 2 large egg whites, lightly beaten
- ¼ cup unsalted whole wheat matzo meal
- ½ teaspoon salt

1 Preheat oven to 350°F. Spray 7 x 11-inch baking dish with nonstick spray.

2 Peel potatoes and cut into 2-inch chunks. Put potatoes and garlic in large saucepan with enough water to cover by 2 inches; bring to boil over high heat. Reduce heat and simmer until potatoes are tender, about 20 minutes. Drain potatoes and garlic, and return to saucepan. Mash with potato masher or large fork until fluffy.

3 Meanwhile, heat oil in large skillet over medium heat. Add onion and cook, stirring occasionally, until softened, about 8 minutes. Add zucchini and cook until tender, about 5 minutes. Add onion mixture, broth, eggs, egg whites, matzo meal, and salt to potatoes in saucepan; stir until blended. Scrape into prepared baking dish. Bake until kugel is heated through and top is lightly browned, about 30 minutes.

Per serving (⅔ cup): 110 Cal, 2 g Total Fat, 1 g Sat Fat, 0 g Trans Fat, 54 mg Chol, 183 mg Sod, 20 g Carb, 3 g Sugar, 2 g Fib, 6 g Prot, 28 mg Calc.

Make Ahead
You can bake the kugel, cool it to room temperature, then cover it tightly with foil and refrigerate up to 2 days. To reheat, bake it, covered, in a preheated 325°F oven until hot, 25 to 30 minutes.

OTHER FESTIVE MENUS

Need a few more reasons to celebrate? We've got 'em! Gather friends and family and give some of the other great party recipes in this book a try. Here are some suggestions for crowd-pleasing menus.

vegetarian thanksgiving
Fragrant Butternut Stew with Apples and Kale, p 95

Savory Lemon-Parsley Millet, p 188

Molasses Pumpkin Pie, p 218

new year's day brunch
Slow-Cooker Apple-and-Sausage Strata, p 9

Creamed Kale with Raisins, p 199

Pear and Pecan Scones, p 21

superbowl sunday
Buffalo Chicken Chili, p 81

Scallion-Walnut Cornbread, p 206

Almond Blondie Bars, p 238

valentines day
Beef Tenderloin with Parmesan Crust, p 135

Caramelized Root Vegetables with Balsamic, p 196

Triple Chocolate Pudding, p 228

st. patrick's day
Throw-it-in-the-Pot Lamb Stew, p 79

Whipped Potato-and-Parsnip Puree, p 251

Bourbon Butterscotch Pudding, p 229 (make it with Irish whisky!)

mother's day
Green Goddess Chicken Salad, p 56

Lemony Roast Potato and Green Bean Medley, p 263

Almond Torte with Mixed Berries, p 211

father's day
Chimichurri-Style Steak Sandwiches, p 31

Slow-Cooker Smoky BBQ Beans, p 265

Pecan Praline Cheesecake, p 212

picnic lunch
Chicken Wraps with Tangy Slaw, p 32

Farro with White Beans, p 193

Peanut Butter–Oatmeal Chocolate Chip Cookies, p 236

kids' birthday party
Mac-and-Cheese Muffins, p 121

Crispy Root Vegetable Chips, p 255

Chocolate Cupcakes with Coconut-Pecan Frosting, p 215

minted pea soup

SERVES 8

2 teaspoons canola oil

2 shallots, thinly sliced

△ 1 (32-ounce) container reduced-sodium chicken broth

△ 1 (16-ounce) bag frozen peas

△ 1 (5-ounce) container baby spinach

△ ½ cup plain fat-free Greek yogurt

¼ teaspoon salt

¼ cup chopped fresh mint

1 Heat oil in large saucepan over medium-high heat. Add shallots and cook, stirring occasionally, until softened, 2–3 minutes. Stir in broth, peas, and spinach; bring to boil. Reduce heat and simmer, stirring occasionally, until peas are tender and spinach is wilted, about 5 minutes.

2 Let mixture cool 5 minutes. Puree, in batches, in food processor or blender. Return soup to saucepan. Stir in yogurt and salt; heat through. Stir in mint just before serving.

Per serving (¾ cup): 93 Cal, 2 g Total Fat, 0 g Sat Fat, 0 g Trans Fat, 0 mg Chol, 141 mg Sod, 13 g Carb, 1 g Sugar, 4 g Fib, 7 g Prot, 30 mg Calc.

For Your Information
This soup is also delicious served chilled. You can refrigerate it up to 3 days, then transfer to bowls and garnish with mint.

roast spring lamb with lavender and honey

SERVES 8

2 tablespoons honey

1 tablespoon chopped fresh rosemary

1 tablespoon minced peeled fresh ginger

2 teaspoons fresh chopped lavender buds

2 garlic cloves, minced

½ teaspoon salt

▲ 1 (2 ½-pound) lean boneless leg of lamb, trimmed, rolled, and tied

▲ 2 red onions, each cut into ½-inch wedges

1 lemon, cut into 6 wedges

½ cup dry white wine

8 small lavender or rosemary sprigs

1 Preheat oven to 400°F. Spray large, deep roasting pan with nonstick spray.

2 Combine honey, rosemary, ginger, lavender, garlic, and salt in small bowl; rub all over lamb. Place lamb in center of prepared roasting pan. Scatter onions and lemon wedges around lamb. Pour wine into pan. Roast until instant-read thermometer inserted into center of lamb registers 145°F for medium, about 1 hour. Transfer lamb to cutting board and let stand 10 minutes.

3 Meanwhile, skim off and discard any fat from pan juices. Cut off strings from lamb and cut lamb into 24 slices. Serve with onion mixture, pan juices, and lavender sprigs.

Per serving (3 slices lamb, ¼ cup onion mixture, and 1 tablespoon pan juices): 222 Cal, 7 g Total Fat, 3 g Sat Fat, 0 g Trans Fat, 91 mg Chol, 262 mg Sod, 6 g Carb, 3 g Sugar, 1 g Fib, 30 g Prot, 27 mg Calc.

Stay On Track

Serve the lamb with a bowl of hot cooked whole wheat couscous. A ½-cup serving per person will increase the *PointsPlus* value by **3.**

lemony roast potato and green bean medley

SERVES 8

- ▲ **2 pounds fingerling potatoes, scrubbed and cut into quarters**
- **4 teaspoons olive oil**
- **2 teaspoons dried oregano**
- **¾ teaspoon salt**
- ▲ **¾ pound thin green beans (haricots verts), trimmed**
- **2 shallots, thinly sliced**
- **Grated zest and juice of 1 lemon**
- **1 tablespoon coarse-grained Dijon mustard**
- **1 tablespoon chopped fresh tarragon**

1 Preheat oven to 425°F. Spray large rimmed baking sheet with nonstick spray.

2 Place potatoes on prepared baking sheet. Drizzle 2 teaspoons oil and sprinkle oregano and ¼ teaspoon salt over potatoes; toss to coat. Spread potatoes evenly and roast until bottoms are golden and crisp, about 30 minutes.

3 Meanwhile, bring large pot of water to boil. Add green beans. Return to boil and cook until green beans are crisp-tender, about 5 minutes. Drain; cool under cold running water and drain again. Pat dry with paper towels.

4 Stir together shallots, lemon zest and juice, mustard, tarragon, remaining 2 teaspoons oil, and remaining ½ teaspoon salt in large bowl until blended. Add potatoes and green beans to bowl and toss to coat. Serve warm or at room temperature.

Per serving (¾ cup): 122 Cal, 3 g Total Fat, 0 g Sat Fat, 0 g Trans Fat, 0 mg Chol, 267 mg Sod, 23 g Carb, 2 g Sugar, 4 g Fib, 3 g Prot, 38 mg Calc.

Make Ahead
You can make the dish up to 1 day ahead and refrigerate in an airtight container. Remove from the refrigerator and let stand at room temperature 1 hour before serving.

citrus chicken under a brick

SERVES 6

july fourth

1 shallot, minced

1 garlic clove, minced

3 tablespoons chopped fresh rosemary

¾ teaspoon salt

3 teaspoons olive oil

1 (4-pound) chicken

Juice of 2 lemons

Juice of 1 orange

2 teaspoons Dijon mustard

1 teaspoon honey

¼ teaspoon red pepper flakes

1 navel orange, cut into 6 wedges

1 Preheat grill: If using gas grill, turn heat under one burner to medium-low. If using charcoal grill, push coals to one side of grill. Wrap 2 clean bricks or outside of large cast-iron skillet in heavy-duty foil.

2 Combine shallot, garlic, 2 tablespoons rosemary, salt, and 1 teaspoon oil in small bowl. With kitchen shears, cut along each side of backbone of chicken; discard backbone. Turn chicken, breast side up, and open flat. Use palm of your hand to flatten breast slightly. With fingers, carefully separate skin on breast, legs, and thighs from meat. Rub shallot mixture on meat under skin, then press skin back in place; tuck wings under chicken.

3 Place chicken, skin side down, on cooler side of grill rack (away from heat source). Place bricks (or cast-iron skillet) on top of chicken and close grill. Grill 40 minutes. Remove bricks and turn chicken over. Grill until instant-read thermometer inserted into thickest part of thigh (not touching bone) registers 165°F, 20–25 minutes longer.

4 Combine lemon juice, orange juice, mustard, honey, pepper flakes, remaining 1 tablespoon rosemary, and remaining 2 teaspoons oil in small bowl until blended. Transfer chicken to platter. Remove and discard skin and wings. Spoon lemon mixture over top. Cut chicken into 6 pieces and serve with orange wedges.

Per serving (1 piece chicken and 1 wedge orange): 231 Cal, 7 g Total Fat, 2 g Sat Fat, 0 g Trans Fat, 102 mg Chol, 444 mg Sod, 10 g Carb, 6 g Sugar, 1 g Fib, 32 g Prot, 38 mg Calc.

slow-cooker smoky bbq beans

SERVES 12

2 slices bacon, coarsely chopped

▲ 1 Vidalia onion, finely chopped

3 garlic cloves, minced

▲ 3 (16-ounce) cans no-salt-added white beans, rinsed and drained

1 cup water

½ cup low-sodium ketchup

1 chipotle en adobo, chopped + 1 tablespoon adobo sauce

3 tablespoons spicy brown mustard

2 tablespoons cider vinegar

1 tablespoon molasses

1 tablespoon packed brown sugar

1 Spray medium skillet with nonstick spray and set over medium-high heat. Add bacon, onion, and garlic. Cook, stirring occasionally, until bacon is browned and onion is softened, about 8 minutes.

2 Transfer onion mixture to 5- or 6-quart slow cooker. Stir in beans, water, ketchup, chipotle en adobo, adobo sauce, mustard, vinegar, molasses, and brown sugar until combined. Cover and cook until flavors are blended and sauce is thickened, 3–4 hours on high or 6–8 hours on low.

Per serving (½ cup): 124 Cal, 2 g Total Fat, 0 g Sat Fat, 0 g Trans Fat, 1 mg Chol, 117 mg Sod, 21 g Carb, 6 g Sugar, 5 g Fib, 6 g Prot, 46 mg Calc.

Make Ahead

You can refrigerate the beans up to 3 days, or freeze up to 3 months. To reheat if frozen, thaw the beans in the refrigerator overnight. Transfer to a saucepan. Cover and cook, stirring occasionally, until beans are heated through.

**SLOW-COOKER SMOKY
BBQ BEANS** p 265

**CITRUS CHICKEN
UNDER A BRICK** p 264

july fourth

**HERB-AND-PARMESAN
GRILLED CORN ON
THE COB** p 268

herb-and-parmesan grilled corn on the cob

SERVES 8

▲ **8 ears of corn**

⅔ cup fat-free mayonnaise

¼ cup grated Parmesan cheese

¼ cup chopped fresh cilantro

Zest and juice of 1 lime

2 teaspoons chili powder

1 Preheat grill to medium-high or prepare medium-hot fire.

2 Gently pull corn husks down to expose kernels, but do not pull husks completely off. Remove silk. Combine mayonnaise, Parmesan, cilantro, lime zest and juice, and chili powder in small bowl. Brush mayonnaise mixture all over corn. Pull husks back over kernels.

3 Wrap each ear of corn in heavy-duty foil. Place on grill rack and grill, turning occasionally, until kernels are very tender, 10–15 minutes.

Per serving (1 ear of corn): 110 Cal, 2 g Total Fat, 1 g Sat Fat, 0 g Trans Fat, 4 mg Chol, 227 mg Sod, 22 g Carb, 5 g Sugar, 3 g Fib, 4 g Prot, 35 mg Calc.

Stay On Track

Looking for an easy grilled vegetable to serve with your meal? Cut 4 medium zucchini into thick slices and place in the center of a large square of heavy-duty foil. Sprinkle with lemon juice, salt, and pepper. Fold the foil over the zucchini and grill the packet alongside the corn.

Recipe Index by *PointsPlus* value

The following recipes work with the Simply Filling technique:

Index